# 23 Shots

# 23 Shots

# The 1894 Shootout
# at Boggs, West Virginia

## Mack Samples

quarrier
press

Charleston, West Virginia

Book and cover design: Mark S. Phillips

Cover background photo courtesy the United States Library of Congress, Reproduction Number: LC-DIG-nclc-04412.

Library of Congress Control Number: 2013934193
ISBN 13: 978-1-891852-89-3
ISBN 10: 1-891852-89-2

10  9  8  7  6  5  4  3  2

Printed in the United States of America

Distributed by:

West Virginia Book Co.
1125 Central Avenue
Charleston, WV 25302

www.wvbookco.com

*There is so much bad in the best of us and so much good in the worst of us...*

**unknown**

# CONTENTS

# ACKNOWLEDGEMENTS

First, I would like to acknowledge W.E.B. Byrne who provided the brief description of the shootout at Boggs in his book *Tale of the Elk*. It was the passages in his book describing the shootout that inspired me to search further into the background and results of the event. Another important reference was Skip Johnson's *River on the Rocks*, which provided some good information about the history of the Birch River country during the 1890s and beyond.

I would also like to acknowledge Ken Sullivan at the West Virginia Humanities Council who accompanied me on a trip to Wise, Virginia to research the background of the men who participated in the shootout on the Birch. Ken is a native of that area. It was important to review the events that led to the eventual shooting. I should also note that the Wise County Historical Society graciously permitted me to browse several volumes, which gave me a better perspective on the area.

Buddy Griffin, nationally known bluegrass fiddler and member of the Samples Brothers Band created the concept for the cover.

David Gillespie, Head Librarian at Frostburg State College and a native of Webster County was very helpful in providing information about the railroad and highway development in central West Virginia during that era.

Mark Romano's excellent *Pictorial History of Webster County* provided me with ideas about what the men from Virginia found when they came into the Birch River area in 1893.

The accounts of the Virginia posse's journey from Wise County to Webster County is based roughly on an oral history account given by one of the surviving posse members, John Branham.

I always acknowledge my good fortune of having an excellent in-house editor and critic in my wife, Thelma, also a native of Webster County.

Finally, hours of perusing the Internet filled in many missing facts about the background of the shooters.

# A NOTE ON WESTERN VIRGINIA AND
# SOUTHEASTERN KENTUCKY ACCENTS

For reasons unknown, various regions develop unique accents and dialects. In the western regions of the Virginia Mountains, where this story begins, some words took on different pronouncements. Words such as *hair* and *there* were spoken with a hard *r*. For example, *hair* became *har* and *there* became *thar*. If you listen to the original Carter Family recordings you will notice these two examples in particular. The Fleming brothers come from that same area of Virginia.

Words such as *about* and *house* tend to lose the *out* sound and take on the *boat* sound. For example, *about* becomes *aboat* and *house* becomes *hoase*.

Adding the letter *n* to words was common not only in Virginia and Kentucky but was also heard in West Virginia in earlier times. Oftentimes, *if* becomes *if 'n*.

Adding the *h* at the beginning of words was also quite common. *It* became *hit*. Some linguists believe this particular practice comes from old English.

Replacing the *a* at the end of a word with a *y* was also very common throughout the Appalachians. Persons whose first name was *Ida* became *Idy*. *Idy* also took the place of the word *idea*. *I ain't got no idy* was a very common phrase throughout the Appalachians and is still heard occasionally. Most other parts of the country would say *I don't have any idea*. Those who travel Interstate 79 though West Virginia will notice a sign identifying a community as *Amma*. Many locals in that area still call it *Ammy*.

There was also a tendency to shorten words a bit. Examples of this are using *probly* for *probably* and *otta* for *ought to*.

Many of these accents and dialects have disappeared in modern times but some still remain. When I was down in western Virginia doing some research for this book, I still heard folks saying *thar* for *there* and *aboat* for *about*.

When writing this narrative I tried to capture some of those accents because I am sure that was how the natives at the time spoke. Accents and dialects are not a sign of a lack of intelligence. They simply reflect the way different areas pronounced words and adopted unique phrases.

I personally think it's kind of sad that everyone now, no matter where they come from, speak like reporters on CNN.

# PROLOGUE

This is a work of fiction but the story is based on historical facts. Most of the characters and events are very real. But the reader should be aware that some literary license has been employed at various points throughout the book. A few of the minor characters are the products of the author's mind as are some of the minor events. However, the major events that occur in the narrative leave little need for creativity. The factual story provides quite enough interest and excitement.

There is ample evidence, albeit some of it taken from oral histories, that the Fleming family was steeped in violence. They were evidently on the fringe of the thriving moonshine business along the northwestern Virginia-southeastern Kentucky border. Although never actually convicted during their youth, Henan and Calvin Fleming were commonly linked to the illegal whiskey business.

When Marshall Taylor, also known as "Red Fox" and "Doc." got himself appointed as a Deputy United States Marshall for the Western Virginia District, he decided that one of the local moonshiners needed to be assassinated. As he planned his strategy, he looked no further than the Fleming brothers for help. He knew they were both quick with a gun, and according to local gossip, both had been linked to local shootings.

Shortly thereafter, Doc Taylor and the Fleming brothers, Henan and Calvin, pulled off what was soon dubbed the "Pound Gap Massacre." If you drive across the mountain from Kentucky to

Virginia on Route 23 today you will see a historical marker alongside the road that provides a brief description of the event.

*23 Shots* is the story of what happened to the three shooters after the Pound Gap incident. In their efforts to avoid arrest, the Fleming brothers ended up in Boggs, WV, a small settlement in Webster County. How and why did they end up in Boggs? What was life like in West Virginia at that time? Who came after them and why? What was the result?

It is interesting to note that attorney Bill Byrne, author of the definitive early history of the Elk River entitled *Tale of the Elk*, became a player in the Fleming brothers' saga. The details of the actual shootout were taken from his account of the trial. The shootout at Boggs rivals the shootout at the OK Corral in Tombstone, Arizona. Yet it never captured the notoriety.

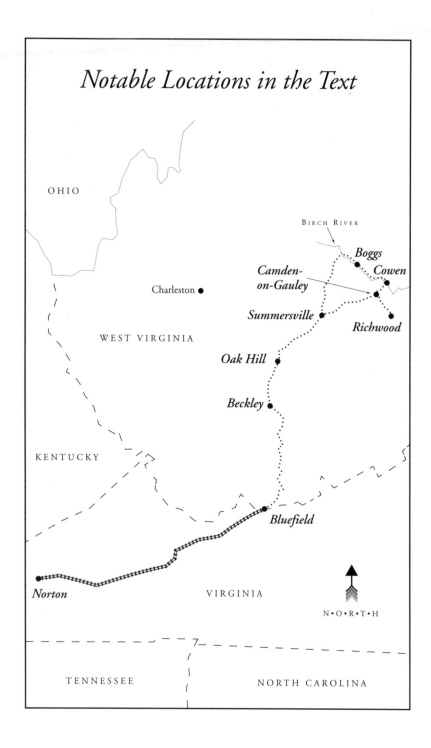

# Notable Locations in the Text

OHIO

WEST VIRGINIA

Charleston •

BIRCH RIVER

Boggs
Cowen

Camden-
on-Gauley

Summersville

Richwood

Oak Hill

Beckley

KENTUCKY

Bluefield

Norton

VIRGINIA

N • O • R • T • H

TENNESSEE

NORTH CAROLINA

# WISE COUNTY VIRGINIA

On the evening of May 13, 1892, Dr. Marshall B. Taylor, a prominent resident of the Pound, Virginia area, waited in his home for the arrival of Calvin Fleming, his brother Henan, and a man by the name of Henry Adams. All three of the expected guests were well-known outlaws of the area. Most of their crimes related to the illegal sale of moonshine whiskey. Dr. Taylor, on the other hand, had for most of his life been a respected citizen of Wise County. While he never attended a medical school, he had studied and trained under a certified doctor by the name of Stallard in nearby Lee County. Such a path to practicing medicine was not unusual in the mountains of Virginia, West Virginia, and Kentucky during that particular era.

Marshall, known as Doctor Taylor, had just begun to practice medicine on his own when the Civil War came crashing down on western Virginia. Marshall Taylor became an officer in the Confederate Army's 64th Cavalry and served four years without any serious injury. Some Civil War writers have classified the 64th as nothing more than a band of outlaws but that is not a documented historical fact.

Taylor returned to Wise County after the war and resumed his medical practice and also became a preacher in the Methodist Church. Taylor preached the gospel in the surrounding environs for several years. He was both well known and respected until his life took a drastic turn in 1876. Everyone was shocked when he was abruptly accused of the murder of a Wise County resident by the name of Robert Moore. Mr. Moore was shot in his own home with his wife looking on. While Mr. Moore was a man of questionable reputation and some considered him an outlaw, Marshall Taylor had no authority to carry out an assassination.

Marshall was arrested and tried for the murder, but lacking any concrete evidence, he was acquitted at a trial by jury. The records show that no direct testimony was given at the trial.

But after the trial, Marshall Taylor took on a different persona. He lost interest in preaching the gospel and practicing medicine. He seemingly began to see himself as a self-appointed official whose task was to rid Wise County of all of its criminal elements. Soon, the United States Marshall for the Western District of Virginia appointed Taylor to be his deputy in Wise County.

Once he got the appointment, he declared war on all of the moonshiners in the area. At that particular time, moonshining was big business in the Virginia and neighboring Kentucky mountains. Marshall Taylor had a big job on his hands.

One pundit of the day called western Virginia and southeastern Kentucky "the moonshine capitol of the world." But Taylor considered himself equal to the task and commenced his eradication program.

One of the most notorious whiskey runners in the area was a man by the name of Ira Mullins who spent some time in Wise County and some time over the Kentucky border in Letcher and Pike Counties. When Marshall got wind of the fact that Ira was going to be passing through Wise Courthouse, as Wise was then called, with a wagonload of shine, he rounded up a posse of volunteers and attempted to intercept and arrest Mr. Mullins. But the Mullins clan resisted and a gun battle erupted. By some accounts over two hundred shots were fired during the melee. Ira Mullins was shot in the back. The driver of the moonshine wagon was killed and another rider on the wagon was also wounded. The moonshiners lost the battle but some of them managed to flee. Ira Mullins survived his wound but was permanently paralyzed.

Soon afterwards, Doc Taylor got word that Ira had sworn to kill him the first chance he got. Some said that the threat put a cold chill into the Doctor's spine and he lived in fear of his life. He knew perfectly well that the Mullins clan was very capable of carrying out the threat. However, time passed and no attempt was made on the deputy's life. Even stranger, there is no record that any attempt was made to arrest Ira Mullins for running whiskey, or for taking part in the war that had erupted in Wise County. One possible explanation for the lack of action was that Ira was probably living up in Letcher or Pike County, Kentucky and was, perhaps, out of the jurisdiction during that time period. But Doc Taylor was spreading the word that Ira had to be dealt with. He began to lay plans to eliminate the Mullins whiskey clan once and for all.

## AT MARSHALL TAYLOR'S HOUSE

During the morning hours of May 12, 1892, Doc Taylor ran into Henry Adams on the street in Wise County Courthouse. He knew Henry more by reputation than by personal contact, but the two men were acquainted. Henry had a reputation for living outside the law. He also enjoyed some notoriety as an excellent shot with a rifle. Doc approached Henry and offered his hand. They exchanged a few pleasant remarks and made a couple of comments about the warm spring weather.

"The mountains are coming alive," said Doc. "I'm just a little weary of this cold rainy weather."

"Me too," Henry answered. "I always look forward to June."

Doc eased into the proposition that had been on his mind since he had received some information the previous evening.

"I know this might be sort of a touchy subject," said Doc, "but do you happen to know where the Fleming boys are hanging out these days?"

Henry hesitated for a moment before he answered. "Yeah, I saw Henan just yesterday. I think he has been hanging around out at his hoase lately."

"What about Calvin? You seen him?"

"No, not lately, but I don't 'spect he'd be hard to find."

"I'd like to talk to those boys for a little bit. You think you could get holt of them and have them come by my hoase this evening? Tell'em I might have a proposition for'em. Tell'em there might be some money in it."

"I'll see what I can do," said Henry.

Henry was a big, broad shouldered guy with a heavy beard and scraggly hair. He was known far and wide as a crack shot with a rifle. At the turkey shoots and rifle competition around the area, the finals usually came down to Henry and Calvin Fleming. Calvin usually beat him, but Henry had won his share. Henry knew the Fleming boys well and was in touch with them almost daily. They had a lot in common. He knew he wouldn't have any trouble finding them. But he didn't know what they would think about going into some sort of deal with Doc Taylor. Everybody knew that Doc was a little eccentric to say the least. But as soon as Doc and Henry parted, Henry got on his horse and rode out to the Henan's place.

"What you up to this morn'n, Henan?" he inquired as he got off his horse.

"Not a hell of a lot," Henan replied. "I was just think'n about getting a little garden started. It's time for that, you know."

"Yeah, I know," Henry replied. "But I ain't much on raising a garden. Dad and them always raise a big one so I just sort of mooch off'n them."

Henan smiled. "That's the way to do it if'n you can git away with it. Looks to me like you need a haircut, Henry. You're start'n to look like a shepherd dog."

"Ah, hell," Henry replied. "Nobody gives a damn what I look like no way."

They both laughed.

"I run into old Doc Taylor in Wise this morning," Henry ventured. "He said he might have some kind of proposition for us."

"What did he mean by us?" asked Henan.

"Well, he said he'd like to talk to me and you and Calvin, said there might be some money in it for us."

"He ain't take'n up moonshining is he?" Henan said with a soft laugh.

"He didn't say what he was a'do'n or what he was aplan'n to do, just said he would like for the three of us to come by his house this evening."

"Well, guess they'd be no harm in a-talk'n with him. I could use a little cash, I reckon. I ain't never liked old Doc much, but we'll see what he's up to. I'll ride over and find Calvin and meet you at Doc's aboat seven o'clock or so."

The sun was about to set over the southwestern mountains when Henan, Calvin, and Henry Adams arrived at Doc's place. They found him sitting on the porch in a straightback chair with his feet up on the banister.

"Evening boys," Doc said without smiling. "Come on up on the porch and find you a chair."

The boys did as requested and found a chair among the many that were scattered about the front porch of Doc's house. There was an uncomfortable silence for several moments before Doc said anything. Finally, he got right to the point.

"You boys know old Ira Mullins, don't you?" he queried.

"Yeah, we know him," Henan answered. "Who the hell don't know him. He's the biggest damn moonshiner in Virginia and half of Kentucky. Now, Cal here knows him better than I do. They've done some business together a time or two. But we know all about old Ira. I guess you damned near killed him a while back."

"That's right," Doc replied. "That's what I wanna talk to you boys about. I need to finish the job. You know that he's a-tell'n everybody that he's going to kill me. I even heard he has put a $300.00 price on my head."

"Yeah, we've heard that," said Calvin.

"Well," Doc continued, "I got word yesterday that him and his clan of outlaws is'a gonna to be coming across Pound Mountain on their way back from Cane Branch over in Letcher County. Ira has been visiting with his brother-in-law. My informer also said that Ira had picked up a load of shine over there and will be a-hauling it over the mountain. The feller who told me said he figured they'd be hauling several barrels of it. Might be a good time to kill the son-of-bitch. If'n he's hauling shine, the law probably wouldn't be too upset about it."

"Where do we fit into this? Henan asked. "Looks like you could shoot him yourself easy enough."

"Hit's a lot more complicated than that," said Doc. "There will probably be eight or ten of them coming along with the wagon. If'n I'd shoot Doc, I'd have a war on my hands. I'd need some help. I know you boys are all good shooters and I'd like to hire you. I've been planning this for a long time. I can give you a hundred dollars apiece if'n you'll help me."

The Fleming boys and Henry Adams looked at one another, almost in disbelief. They had been involved in a lot of illegal activity and some shooting scrapes, but no one had ever asked them to shoot anybody for money.

"I don't know," said Henan. "We ain't never been involved with git'n paid to shoot anybody."

"Well, think of it this way," said Doc, "you would be getting rid of that clan of heathens. They ain't never been noth'n com'n to that Mullins outfit. They's just riffraff. Always have been. We'd be doing the county a big favor if'n we got rid of all of'em."

Henan stared at Doc for a minute or two. Finally, he ventured a sentence. "I think me and Cal and Henry ought to go out in the yard and talk about this for a minute or two before we answer you. This is some pretty serious stuff here."

"You go right ahead and talk all you want," said Doc. "But I've got to have an answer this evening. If you boys don't want to do it, I'll have to look elsewhere."

The boys retreated to the yard, out underneath a big box elder tree that was just starting to come out in leaf. They discussed some things that could go wrong with the deal and also the possibility that one of them might get killed. They figured that there might be a good shooter among the Mullins clan. Calvin and Henry were all for it, but Henan was reluctant. But after knocking the idea around for a few minutes, he relented.

"The truth is old Doc ain't no better than Ira so I don't know that we'd be doing the county a favor. But a hundred dollars is a pretty good pile of money," said Henan. "Let's go for it."

The boys went back up on the porch and told Doc Taylor that they were in. At Doc's suggestion they all agreed to meet up at the foot of the southern side of Pound Mountain about twilight on the next evening. Doc said they could ride up near the gap and make camp before it got dark.

"I figure the Mullins clan will be coming through the gap around noon and we will need some time during the morning to make some preparations. I want this thing to go off without a hitch."

# THE POUND GAP AMBUSH

Henan and Calvin arrived at the agreed upon spot about 6:00 p.m. the next evening, May 13, 1892. Doc was sitting on his horse waiting for them when they arrived. "Evening boys," he said without a grin. "Nice spring evening ain't it."

"It shore to hell is that," Calvin replied.

"Where's Henry?" asked Doc.

"We ain't seen him since yesterday," said Henan. "He said he'd meet us up here."

"Well, he'll probably show up sometime," said Doc. "If'n he don't show up pretty soon we'll ride on up without him."

The three men waited several minutes but Henry did not appear. They rode on up the mountain before dark and got to the place that Doc had in mind for the ambush.

"I think this will be a good spot," said Doc. "We can lay low here until we see'em acom'n and start shoot'n when they get close enough. I'm not sure how many they will be or how well armed they are, but it's my idy that if'n we all start shoot'n we can nail them before they git a chance to shoot back. I guess you boys have got your rifles in good shape."

"Yeah, we always keep our rifles in good shape," said Henan. "We brought plenty of shells in case we get into a long, drawed-out battle."

"It might be a good idy if we'd set up a little blind along the top of these rocks. They might spot us otherwise. We can work on that in the morning."

Doc Taylor and the Fleming brothers spent the night near the rocks where they planned to attack the next morning. They camped without a fire and slept with their heads on their saddles. The next morning, as Doc had suggested, they set about the task of cutting off some brush and stacking it on top of the rocks. The trees and brush were not yet out in full leaf but there was enough foliage on them to put up a fairly good screen. Once they had constructed the crude blind to their satisfaction they all retreated down to where the Fleming boys had tied their horses, well back away from the road. Cal and Henan got out their rifles and looked them over. They both carried nice looking Winchester 73s.

"Them's fine look'n rifles," said Doc.

"We take a lot of pride in our guns," said Henan.

"I've always heard that you boys were good shots, some say the best in the country."

"I wouldn't know about that," said Henan, "but we do all right, I reckon."

Henry Adams never showed. Calvin allowed as how he might have lost his nerve. He was the one who was most in favor of the idea in the first place so the Fleming boys were a little surprised that he did not show.

"We can pull it off just fine without him," said Doc, "if we watch what we're a-doin'. The first target will be old Ira himself. We've got to make sure that we kill that old bastard first. Then we'll shoot however many more is necessary. But we have to keep in mind that somebody is probably going to shoot back if they are able, so once we start shoot'n, we'd better get all of them that we can."

The three shooters positioned themselves behind the fortress that they had constructed and waited. The Mullins clan's arrival was a little later than Doc had anticipated. The Fleming boys noticed that Doc was getting antsy. He kept walking back and forth behind the wall of rocks.

It was a long steep pull up the north side of the mountain. Cal and Henan figured that the Mullins Clan would have to make several stops to rest the horses. They didn't know if they had a two or four horse team, but if only two horses were pulling the wagon, it would be slow going. The three men waited and watched, munching on some old corn bread and dried meat that Calvin had brought along. Sometime around 1:00 p.m. they heard voices and saw the wagon coming about a hundred yards away.

Ira Mullins, who was mostly paralyzed, was sitting atop the wagon on some hay or straw, enjoying the sunshine and the mountain scenery. A man by the name of John Chappel was driving the wagon while Ira's wife and son sat near the front of the wagon.

Ira's daughter-in-law was walking just a few yards in front of the wagon. Straggling along behind the wagon was Ira's 15-year-old son and Greenberry Harris, a man who had been doing some work for Ira.

When the wagon came nearly alongside the makeshift fortress just a few feet away, the firing commenced. The three shooters all wore masks over their faces. They unleashed a barrage of gunfire. The daughter-in-law, Jane Mullins managed to flee the scene. She was not hit. John Harrison Mullins, fifteen-year-old son of Ira, also escaped injury even though his suspenders were shot in two as he ran down the mountain. But everyone else in the entourage was killed. Ira was hit multiply times, literally shot all to pieces. All of the others who were slain were also hit several times. Even the two-horse team pulling the wagon was shot dead.

The shooters mounted their horses and fled the scene, but not before they had searched the wagon and took a sack of money that the Mullins family had with them. Some accounts say the amount taken was between $700 and $1,000. Doc gave the Fleming boys three hundred dollars each. The boys separated themselves from Doc Taylor and fled deep into the mountains of Letcher County up in Kentucky and never saw him again. Henan and Calvin knew lots of people up that way and knew that they could lay low there until things blew over a bit down in Wise County.

# THE HEAT IS ON

When word of the massacre arrived in Wise, there was a big reaction. Even though Ira Mullins was not a model citizen, no one approved of the outright slaughter of five people.

A large posse was organized soon after Jane Mullins had given her account of the shooting and identified the shooters as Doc Taylor and the Fleming Brothers. At one point in the search for the killers, Calvin and Henan were located in the mountains and an attempt was made to capture them. But a gun battle erupted. Henan was wounded but he and Calvin managed to escape. One newspaper account from Clintwood, Virginia, said that four members of the posse of twenty-two were killed during the arrest attempt.

For the next several months Henan and Calvin managed to elude or outshoot their pursuers. But the law kept the pressure on the boys and for many months they were living the life of desperate fugitives. They finally decided that they had to leave the area.

Doc Taylor, now locally called "Red Fox" because he was so sly, made his way back to his home in Wise and hid out in his attic. He was fed and protected there by his wife and son. His son finally decided that he was going to have to get Doc out of the area. Plans were made to put him on a boxcar in Norton, Virginia and let him ride up to Bluefield, West Virginia where he could hop another train to the south. Doc's son gave him sixty dollars in travel money and put him in the boxcar. But someone saw Doc being put on the train and sent a telegram to Bluefield. It was actually a local attorney who wired the Baldwin Detective Agency in Bluefield. W. G. Baldwin arrested Doc Taylor as he attempted to catch a boxcar south. He was delivered back to Wise County and put in the local jail.

Henan Fleming, still at large, rode into his own yard on his horse on September 18, 1893 and walked slowly into his house. He hung his hat on one of the pegs beside the door and his holstered revolver on the next one. He did not say anything when he came in and his wife Catherine gave him a wary look. She had not seen Henan for several days and he had been in and out of the place for several months. He and his brother Calvin had been hiding out in the high country for nearly a year.

"I'm gonna git the hell out of hrar," he announced as he found a chair at the kitchen table. "I'll have to leave you by yourself till I can git settled someplace."

"Why have you decided to go now?" Catherine exclaimed as she gave him a puzzled look.

"Well, you know that me and Cal have had several narrow escapes since we been accused of being in on that big shootout up at Pound Gap. You also know damned good and well that we didn't have nary a thing to do with it. That wider woman of Wilson Mullins swears on a stack of Bibles that she saw me and Cal up there with the shooters. She said that even though all of the men had their faces covered, she was pretty sure it was us, said she could tell by our body shape and the way we were a'stand'n. They have been trying to track us down for several months. So far we have dodged'em but we just learned that they is a $700 reward out for our arrest and conviction."

Catherine had heard several stories about the attempts to capture Henan and Calvin. So far the two brothers had managed to outflank the pursuers, or according to some accounts had killed those who came after them. Catherine was particularly concerned about the newspaper account from Clintwood, which had stated that the brothers had killed four of the five detectives who went after them on one occasion. There were rumors swirling everywhere about shootouts that had occurred while trying to arrest them. Another account from a Richmond newspaper reported that both Henan and

Calvin had both been mortally wounded.

"But can't you prove that you didn't have anything to do with it?" Catherine inquired.

"Probably won't have airy chance to try to prove it. I'm pretty sure Cap Hall will be com'n for us. You know how old Cap is. He hates me and Cal and this mess we are in will give him the perfect excuse to kill us. He don't give a damn about the law or justice."

"But where will you go?" asked Catherine, "and what will you do?"

"Cal and I have been talking about it all day," said Henan. "We could go up into West Virginia. We got family up there, you know, at some place called Boggs. Now I ain't got the slightest notion where the hell Boggs is but I know hits located deep in the West Virginia mountains. I don't think anyone would ever find us thar. The word is that they's a lot of logging gone on up in them parts and we could more than likely find something to do. I'll leave you some money and send you more once I get settled in. Later, you could come up and jine me. We could git a fresh start up there and git shut of all them people down in Pound and Wise that don't like us."

"I don't know, Henan," Catherine said solemnly. "When would you go?"

"We'll take off early in the morning," said Henon. "We can ride the horses down to Norton and sell them. We'll hop that afternoon freight that goes through Norton and ride up to Bluefield. I guess oncet we git to Bluefield, we'll just have to find our way to Boggs. I know hits located on the Birch River and I seen in one of the letters my brother-in-law sent that hits in Webster County. Me and Cal ain't stupid. We can find our way. If'n we need to, we'll buy a couple of horses somewhere if'n we run out of railroad and ride horseback on into Boggs."

Although Catherine was terrified at the thought of Henan and Cal taking off for unknown parts and leaving her behind, she tried to hide it. She knew full well that Henan was probably right about Big Ed (Cap) Hall and his friends. Doc Taylor had been caught and was housed in jail. She knew Henan and Cal would not give up. She knew that someone, on one side or the other, was going to get killed. Cap Hall was known to be a violent man and Henan and Cal were not exactly Sunday school boys. The Fleming boys had an area-wide reputation for being wild and reckless in their behavior. They had been in trouble with the law several times, mostly concerning moonshine whiskey, and everyone knew they were always heavily armed. So the more Catherine thought about Henan's plan of leaving the area, the more she thought that it was a good idea. She didn't know how she was going to handle being alone, but if worse came to worse, she figured she could always go back to her mom and dad's place. She spent the remainder of the evening helping Henan get his things together, sometimes fighting back tears as she went about it. Henan stuffed a change of clothes, some underwear, a jacket, and his razor into his saddlebags. He planned to travel pretty light. Catherine spent some time preparing some food for the brothers to take with them. Neither of them slept a wink during the night. Catherine held onto Henan the whole night through, thinking that it might be the last time they would ever be in each other's arms.

They had been married six years. It had, at times, been a stormy marriage. She never knew where he was half the time and had heard whispers that Henan had fooled around with other women. But she had remained the faithful wife. He and Cal were always going off for three or four days at a time and she had no idea where they were. But Henan always came home and always appeared to be glad to be there. Catherine thought that in his own way, Henan really did love her though she had never heard him use that word. Love was, in fact, a word rarely used among the mountain people. Catherine could not recall ever hearing anyone speaking the phrase "I Love You," when she was growing up so she never expected to hear it from Henan. It was just the way mountain folks were. Sometimes men would remark to one another that they "thought a lot of" some particular girl, but they never said they loved her.

While Henan and Calvin were somewhat wild and aimless with

their lives, and often lived outside the law, they were not lazy. Even though they sometimes tried to avoid hard work, they were both quite capable with their hands and both had made a good living. Catherine was never quite sure where Henan got some of his money, but he always seemed to have plenty of it. As he was preparing his departure the next morning, Catherine inquired about how he was going to finance his trip.

"Cal and I have a little money ahead," he told her. "We have laid some back. Like I said, we'll sell them horses in Norton. When we git as far as we can on the train we'll buy us a couple more and find our way."

Catherine noticed that he had put his .44 caliber pistol in a little shoulder type holster, which would be concealed by his jacket. He rarely went anywhere without his pistol. Calvin was even more capable with a pistol than he was a rifle. Catherine was much more concerned about the boys getting lost on the way to Boggs than she was about anyone bringing harm to them. Although she had never actually seen Henan in action, she had heard from several sources that he came across as very friendly and harmless on a person to person basis, but that he could also be a very rough when the occasion called for it.

Calvin also left a wife and family behind. He did not really want to make the flight to West Virginia and resisted at first. But both of the Fleming boys saw the heat coming down on them and realized that if they stayed in the area it was going to come to a bad end. As Henan told him when they were discussing the possible trip to West Virginia, "sooner or later, one of us is going to get killed or captured if we hang around."

# WEST VIRGINIA BOUND

The Fleming brothers knew that they could not ride through Wise Court House so they skirted around the town. They knew the country quite well. Once they cleared the populated areas, they turned their horses toward Norton, Virginia. It was August 9, 1893 when they rode into Norton. It was nearly an all day trip because they tried to keep off the main roads as much as they could. Once they got into Norton they felt fairly safe. They were not well known down that way and figured that no one would recognize them. But they still moved around the town cautiously.

Henan and Calvin were both fairly good-looking boys. Henan was the taller of the two, around six feet. He was also the most engaging. He had a nice way of greeting people. Although he did not have a broad smile, he could always manage a pleasant half-grin when he met strangers. He also had very penetrating eyes. Calvin, while not quite as imposing, was also a pleasant looking fellow. They both wore their hair short and were clean-shaven. Both of them were blessed with lean sinewy bodies and displayed a swagger when they walked. It was said that Calvin, while smaller, was the tougher of the two in a physical fight. But he did not fight fair. Anytime he had been in a fight he either used the butt of his gun, or secured whatever he could get a hold of and use it as a club. He had also been known to use a knife. There was a rumor around Pound that he and Ira Mullins had once killed a Syrian peddler and took all of his goods and money. The peddler had been stabbed. But no one had ever actually penned the deed onto Calvin.

It was a warm August evening so the boys decided to ride back a ways from the city limits and camp for the night. They rode back into Norton early the next morning in the bright sunshine. As they rode into town they discussed the fact that they were going to have a long and uncertain day. They decided that they had better get a good breakfast under their belts before plunging into their adventure. They both enjoyed a platter of ham, eggs, grits, bacon and biscuits. Henan talked to the proprietor after they had finished their meal about where they might be able to sell a couple of horses. The restaurant owner directed them just a couple of blocks down the street.

They had no trouble selling their mounts. They were both good horses and the boys were ready to take a fairly low price for them. There was very little negotiating. They sold the horses and saddles for forty dollars each and were soon on their way. They both now had about $300 in their pockets. They flung their saddlebags over their shoulders and were underway for West Virginia.

They walked down to the rail yard. Even though they knew about when the freight train rolled out, they did not want to take any chances so they wanted to check out the schedule. After confirming the schedule, they decided to place themselves down the track a ways before they tried to board. They wanted the train to be moving when they hopped on but they did not want it moving too fast. They decided on a spot just out of town where there was a small grove of trees. When they arrived at the chosen spot, they discussed their strategy.

"I think we need to get on opposite sides of the tracks," said Henan. "We'll be able to see each other underneath and when I see an opening, I'll give you a signal. We don't have to board the same car."

"Sounds good to me," said the always-agreeable Calvin, who had hopped freights before. "I like them coal cars. There's a pretty snug place on either end of them where a man can hump up and be pretty comfortable."

"That'll be OK," said Henan. "But if I see what looks like an empty box car with a door open, I might try that. Guess we'll just wait and see what's open."

The brothers waited in the trees until they heard the freight engine blow the steam whistle and start slowly chugging its way forward. It did not appear to be an extremely long train and there were a lot of coal cars. They positioned themselves on either side of the track and waited till the engine passed before they made their move. They were both keenly aware of the fact that some of the brakemen carried a billy club so they did not want to be seen boarding.

The train was moving along at a clip just slightly faster than a man would walk when they made their move. Calvin grabbed hold of a coal car and Henan, not spotting a box car, snagged another coal car just behind the one that Calvin had boarded.

It was a bright warm day so they rode along in reasonable comfort. Every time the train made a stop, they jumped off and hid somewhere near the track. A couple of times they watched a brakeman walk alongside the train up toward the engine and back. He was definitely looking for hobos.

After it got dark, the boys decided to stay aboard during stops, figuring that the nosey brakeman would not see them. About twenty miles from Bluefield, the big freight made a stop in a rather desolate area to take on water. The brakeman, with a long club in his hand, made a walk down the left side of the train where Calvin was humped up on the end of a coal car. The brakeman spotted him and yelled for him to get down. Henan, on the opposite side of the train heard the yell and made his way underneath the car in which he was riding.

As the brakeman approached Calvin with his club drawn back Henan grabbed him from behind and pinned his arms behind him. Calvin drew his gun and slugged the brakeman on the top of his head. He went limp in Henan's arms. The Fleming boys rolled the man down a steep embankment.

"We'd better git the hell off'n this train," said Henan. "Oncet they discover that brakeman is missing, they'll be look'n for us for sure. Nobody's seen us yet so we'd better scat."

"Where the hell are we?" Calvin asked.

"I ain't exactly sure, but I'd say we can't be too far from the West

Virginia line. Oncet the train goes ahead, we can follow the tracks into the next town."

They walked into Bluefield on August 12 during the early afternoon in a slight drizzle. They located a hotel, rented a room, and took a bath and shaved. That evening, after they enjoyed a good supper, Henan talked to some locals about catching a train up to Webster County, but he soon learned that such a train did not exist. They walked back to their hotel room somewhat discouraged.

"I thought sure we could catch some kind of a train out of here that would take us close to Boggs, but I guess that ain't the case," said Henan.

"Sure don't sound like it," Calvin replied. "I reckon those fellers we talked to knowed what the hell they're talking about. Guess we are either going to have to buy us a couple of horses or else start walking."

"I don't think I want to walk that far," said Henan. "There's probably a bunch of steep hills to climb twixt here and Boggs."

"I ain't a-want'n to walk no farther than I have to," Calvin replied.

The next morning they located a livery stable and purchased a couple of horses and saddles for forty-five dollars each. They were actually better mounts than the ones they sold in Norton. They asked the stable owner if he knew the best way to get to Boggs. Henan did all the talking.

"I don't know a place called Boggs," he replied. "Do you know what county it's in?"

"Yep, hits in Webster County," Henan replied. "I think on the Birch River."

"Well, I can point you toward Webster County," the stable man said, "but I'm not familiar with Birch River. I can put you on the road to Beckley, up in Raleigh County."

From there, I think you can take a road up to Fayetteville. From Fayetteville, there's a road of sorts that will take you over the mountain and you will come out on the Weston-Gauley Bridge Turnpike just east of a place called Gauley Bridge. You can then follow the turnpike to Summersville, which is in Nicholas County.

"From there, I wouldn't know what to tell you except that Nicholas County borders Webster County so you'll be close. From Beckley I'd say you are looking at a two to three day ride on horseback. You'll be going through a lot of coal mining country. The roads are going to be bad. If it rains, they'll be plenty of mud. They'll be some stretches where folks are pretty scarce so I'd be prepared to camp out a night or two. If you don't mind me ask'n, why are you headed up that way?"

"We're much obliged, to you," said Calvin. "I think we'll find our way. We got folks up that way that we will be visiting."

"Good luck to you," the stable man said as they shook hands and parted.

As they were riding out of town, Henan decided that they might ought to purchase a few supplies.

"Since we may have to camp along the way a couple of times, Calvin," Henan said. "We'd better pick up some supplies. We probly need to buy us a couple of cheap blankets. It might get pretty cool up in the mountains this time of the year oncet the sun goes down. And I'll tell you something else. Hit won't be long till that old blue northern will blow and you know good and well what that feels like. I'd say it will be a little colder in Boggs than it gits down in Wise County. We ain't got no winter clothes with us so we probly ought to think about that. We may not be able to find a store that sells clothes oncet we leave Bluefield."

"I'd say there's a pretty good chance of some cool nights," Calvin replied. "I don't like to think about freezing my ass off along some creek bank somewhere. And you're right about git'n some winter duds. We need to think about that."

They found a big general store and purchased some items that would be easy to carry along with them. They decided not to buy a heavy coat or anything bulky that would be difficult to carry. But they did purchase some long-handled underwear and winter hats with flaps that would pull down over their ears. They decided to take a chance on finding winter coats after they got to Webster County. They didn't find much in the way of food that could be carried along. They did find some canned beans and some cheese and crackers. They figured that would keep them from starving until they got to Beckley.

# RAIN AND MUD

It started to rain a little after they got a few miles north towards Beckley. Neither of the Fleming brothers had packed or purchased a slicker or any kind of a raincoat so they were both wet in just a few minutes. They stopped and put the blankets they had bought under their saddles so they would stay dry. The road was muddy even when they first started the journey. In some places it was nearly a quagmire. The rain increased steadily as they rode north. Henan pulled his hat a little forward so the rain would run off better. Neither of them had exchanged a word for a half-an-hour or so. Finally, Calvin pulled up underneath a big white oak tree that was standing near the road.

"We're gonna have to get out of this rain for a while or everything we have is going to be wringing wet," he said to Henan. "I ain't seen a building of any kind for the last five or six miles."

"Maybe we had just better look for some shelter," said Calvin. "We ought to find us a rock cliff somewhere. Surely to God there's one around in these steep mountains. Keep you eyes up agin the hills and see if you can spot something. This damned rain's git'n serious."

They forged ahead without speaking for a couple of more miles before Calvin pointed to an overhanging rock on the left side of the road. It was about 50 yards up the hillside. They dismounted and led the horses up toward it. The overhang was actually pretty large and afforded ample room for both the men and their horses. It was dry underneath the rock and they noticed that it had been used before because they saw the remains of a campfire.

"Boy, we could sure to hell use a fire to dry stuff out a little bit.

My clothes are soaking wet," said Henan as he pulled the saddle off his horse. "I doubt that we will be able to find any wood dry enough to get a fire going."

"Don't give up so easy," said Calvin as he stashed his saddle against the solid wall of rock at the back of the overhang. "I'll poke around a little and see if I can find something that'll burn. There's always something that will burn up under a log somewhere, or maybe in a pine thicket."

Calvin did manage to find some dry wood scattered about the hillside and they soon had a fire going. They both took off their trousers and shirts. Henan found some sticks to hang them on so the wet clothes would dry by the fire. The change of clothes they had packed in their saddlebags remained dry so they were able dress while their wet clothes dried. The canned beans they had purchased before they left Bluefield came in handy. They ate sparingly before leaning back against the rocks to rest. Their idea of putting their blankets under their saddles had worked to some extent. The blankets had remained fairly dry but they were a little damp around the edges. The brothers spent the night catching short naps in between tending the fire and shifting their clothes around so they would dry better. The rain stopped during the night. They could see glimpses of the moon through the clouds before dawn.

The morning brought a new lease on life for them as they put the clothes that were mostly dry into their saddlebags. From what the stable man had told them, they figured they could easily make it to Beckley before nightfall.

They made good time during the morning hours even though the road was muddy and, at times, rutted out. They met very few people. Along about noon they pulled up in a field alongside the road. It looked to be a hayfield that someone had harvested in late summer. There was some new growth.

"We'd better let these horses pick a little bit," said Calvin.

"Good idea," Henan answered. "We ain't in no gawd-awful hurry that I know of. Ain't nobody gonna know us up in this neck of the woods. Let's let'em graze for a hour or two before we go on."

They tethered the horses and walked down by a little stream at the lower end of the meadow and sat down on some rocks.

"One thing about that rain yesterday," said Calvin. "It was a warm rain. At least we didn't freeze our ass off."

"Right," Henan replied. "In fact it felt kinda good rid'n along in it. The damned mud is the worst part."

"It won't kill us," said Calvin. "We're doing good so far. But it sure would have been nice if we could have found a train that would have take'n us a little closer to Boggs. I ain't never rode a horse as far as we have to go and I 'spect I'll get tired of it afore we git thar."

"I'd say we'll both be mighty glad to git offen them horses," Henan replied. "It might be a hard trip but it'll be better than git'n shot at down in Wise County, or worse yet, git'n hanged."

Calvin smiled a little. "Yeah, I guess we're do'n OK. But I hope to hell no one saw us leave Wise County. You know someone spotted old Doc Taylor when he left and they were wait'n for him at Bluefield."

"Yeah, I know," Henan replied. "We need to keep a wary eye over our shoulder all the time. But I think we got away slick. I hope you didn't kill that brakeman when you hit him in the head," said Henan.

"I don't think I hurt him much, didn't hit him that hard. Leastwise, we never heard noth'n about it when we got to Bluefield. He might have come around afore the train left the water tank. He didn't see you at all and I doubt that he got much of a look at me. It was fairly dark."

"Wherever he is, I'd bet he has a sore head," said Henan with a smile.

"Let's tie them horses a little better and hone up our shoot'n eye before we go," Calvin suggested. "You never know what we might git into along the way."

"Good idy," Henan replied.

They walked along the creek until they spotted a poplar tree that was about as broad as a man's body and decided it would do for some shooting practice. They positioned themselves about 25 or 30 feet back from the tree.

"You go first," said Calvin. "Just pretend that tree is old Cap Hall a-com'n after you."

Henan spread his legs a little, grabbed the .44 from his shoulder holster and fired twice. Calvin walked up to the tree to take a look.

"One of the slugs would've got him shore. But one of them might have just nicked him a little."

"Your turn," said Henan.

Calvin looked at the tree and turned his back to it. He grabbed his .44, spun around, and fired three rounds in quick succession.

They both walked to the tree and found all three slugs in the center of the tree within about a three-inch area.

"You always could outshoot me with a pistol," said Henan. "But I think I could whoop your ass in a fair fight."

"You might, but you know I don't believe in fight'n fair," Calvin replied.

## FAYETTE COUNTY HOSPITALITY

The boys rode into Beckley looking for a place to stay as twilight was closing in. Beckley was not a very big town but it did offer several places to lodge. They found a spot that they agreed on, and signed in as Walter and Frank Johnson. They inquired as to where they could stable their horses, and the desk clerk directed them to a stable down at the end of the street. The stableman was not quite as friendly as the one in Bluefield, but Henan, using his winning ways, managed to get some answers out of him.

"I don't know nothing about Boggs," the stableman said. "But if you say its in Webster County, you'd have to take the road up to Fayetteville, then ride over to Gauley Bridge and pick up the Weston-Gauley Bridge Turnpike."

"Yeah, someone else mentioned that turnpike to us," said Henan.

"It'll take you up to Summersville. I'm not exactly sure, but I think that turnpike continues on north and crosses that Birch River that you mentioned. When you get to Summersville, you'll be close to Webster County and somebody there can point you in the right direction. That's about all I can tell you."

"I reckon that'll help some," said Henan. "That's more than we knowed before we stopped here."

"Now that Turnpike is rougher'n hell in some places. You'll have some mountains to go over."

Calvin gave him a steely stare. "We ain't no strangers to mountains," he said. "We grew up in them." He didn't say where. He figured there was no use advertising where they were from.

The Virginia boys rode out the next morning in fairly pleasant weather and headed toward Oak Hill. A hot bath and a good shave had put them in a better mood. Even though there had been no rain for several hours, the road was a muddy mess. Sometimes the mud was up over the hooves of the horses so it was slow going. They figured out that they could make better time if they stayed a little off the road and rode close to the hillside. But there was so much brush growing outward that they had to stay in the middle of the road more often than not.

When they rode into Oak Hill they discovered that the streets were worse than the roads. The main drag was rutted out badly from wagon tracks. The mud was mixed with manure and produced an awful smell. They decided that they did not want to spend much time in Oak Hill.

They made a brief stop at a small restaurant on the north side during the early afternoon and headed on toward Fayetteville on the mud-soaked road. The sun was extra warm in mid-afternoon and lightning was flashing to the south. The thunder was way behind the lightning so they knew that the rain was not close. Calvin kept watching the sky with a wary eye.

"I'd hate like hell to git wet agin and have to sleep under a rock cliff," he said as he rode up alongside his brother.

"Me to," Henan replied. "We ought to keep our eye out for a place where we might git underoof for the night. I don't know whar that would be cause I ain't seen many hoases since we left Oak Hill."

As they rode on it was obvious that the storms were moving toward them. Although they couldn't be sure, they figured they had covered about five or six miles since leaving Oak Hill. Finally, they spotted a dwelling sitting about a hundred yards back on the right hand side of the road. It was a small, solid looking dwelling. The outside appeared to be covered with rough sawn oak and there were strips covering the cracks where the boards had come together. Wood shingles covered the roof and there was a nice front porch. There was a barn and some outbuildings in a cluster about twenty-five yards from the house. As they ventured up the little road that led up to the place they also noticed a milk cow, chickens, and a large garden area. There was a picket fence around the house enclosing the small yard.

"Let's ride in and ask if we can hole up in the barn until the storms roll through," said Henan. "They might run us off, but it won't hurt to ask."

"I'm game if'n you are," Calvin replied. "You know it might be a good idea if we stashed our guns in our saddlebags. Folks might get offended if they'd git a gander at our .44s."

They climbed off their horses before they left the road and put their pistols in their saddlebags. They remounted and as they neared the house they noticed two small children playing in the yard. Their horses scattered chickens all over the place as they approached the picket fence. When the kids saw the horses they took off for the house, yelling something. Henan smelled a hog pen and spotted it a little ways from the barn.

A woman came out on the porch and looked at them. She did not say anything. She just looked them over.

"Howdy," Henan ventured with his pleasant grin. "We're a couple of strangers a-pass'n through on our way to Webster County. We were a-wondering if'n we might hole up in your barn till the storms pass. We won't be no trouble."

The woman continued to look them over carefully. They did not look too bad because they had cleaned up some in Beckley, but their pants were covered with mud and the horses were a muddy mess. The boys were still sitting astraddle of their mounts. Finally, after an almost too long silence, the woman spoke. "Git down if'n you're of a mind to and come on in the yard. I'll have to speak to my husband. He's feeling poorly and has tak'n to his bed." She disappeared into the small house.

"Not a bad looking heifer, is she?" said Henan.

"Nope," Calvin replied. "She's passable fer sure."

When the woman came back through the door the two small children were hanging onto her dress, trying to stay hidden. The rumbling thunder had turned into keen cracks close behind the flashes of lightning.

"My husband says you're welcome to put up in the barn. Ain't nothing in there but the horse and milk cow. They come and go as they please. They may come in from the storm. You can get in the dry there and stay as long as you need to."

"We're certainly much obliged," said Henan. "We'll probly head on out oncet the storm passes."

"There's some feed in there if you want to feed your horses a little," she said as they led the horses toward the barn.

It was getting along toward 5:00 p.m. when they got settled. The storm persisted and eventually brought on a regular gully washer. The little stream that ran by the house was roaring in no time. The lightning was fierce. The boys were very thankful to have shelter. They stripped the saddles from their mounts and leaned back against one of the stalls and watched the storm through the open door.

The storm finally did begin to settle down and the rain slacked to a slight drizzle. Some cooler air came in behind the storm. As Calvin and Henan were starting to think about saddling up, the woman of the house came through the barn door.

"My husband says to tell you that you're welcome to sleep here in the barn tonight," she said. "It's gonna be awful wet on the road and you are not liable to find a dry place to sleep. He says he's sorry he can't come and talk to you."

"What ail's him?" Calvin inquired.

"Well, he hurt his back work'n in a little old coal mine down the road here a piece a week or so ago. He feels OK, just can't get around much. I think he's some better, but he's awful worried about keeping the place up. I've been doing the milk'n and such. You boys are also welcome to take supper with us. We ain't got much else but we got a-plenty to eat. We had an awful good garden this year and my husband just killed a hog afore he hurt himself."

"That's mighty generous of you to offer supper," said Henan as he looked at Calvin.

"I ain't gonna turn down a meal," said Calvin.

"We'll be obliged to eat with you," said Henan. "By the way, my name is Henan Fleming and this here is my brother Calvin. We rode up out of Virginia to visit some kin up in Webster County." He figured it was safe enough to use their own names out in the rural areas.

"My name is Sally," the woman replied. "My husband calls me Sally Ann. My husband, his name is Caleb, Caleb Johnson. Supper will be on the board in about a half hour. You're welcome to come set on the porch."

The boys looked at each other with a smile. It was really odd that these people had the same name that they had chosen to call themselves. They were glad they used their real names.

"Thanks," said Henan. "We'll be up in a bit."

As the woman headed toward the house, Henan looked her over again. "She's right please'n to look at, damned if she ain't. I'll bet she's a good cook too."

"I hope she is," Calvin replied. "I'm as hungry as an old boar bear in March. You better stop staring at that heifer when you get in the house. Her husband might not approve."

"I'll be good," Henan smiled.

Calvin and Henan were a little surprised when they entered the house. Everything was clean and neat. The inner walls were covered with wallpaper giving the house a cheery look. There looked to be two small bedrooms going off the living area. A nice piece of stonework housed the fireplace.

The spread on the table was quite impressive. The meal consisted of some kind of pork meat, boiled potatoes, green beans, turnips, and some tomatoes. There was a big pan of cornbread coming out of the oven. Caleb Johnson came out of one of the rooms holding onto things as he walked, obviously in pain. He was a small but powerfully built man with a heavy head of dark hair. His demeanor was pleasant and he forced a smile as he sat down at the table. No one offered any grace. Mr. Johnson just started passing things around.

"Where you say you boys are head'n?" Mr. Johnson inquired.

"Guess we're gone to a place called Boggs," said Henan. "Since we've come into West Virginia, we notice that ain't nobody ever heard of it. We have kin there that we ain't seen in a while. Guess it's located on the Birch River in Webster County."

"Well, it ain't too far to Webster. I've been up around Summersville quite a bit. It's in Nicholas County and I know Webster is the next county over. You can make it into Summersville from here easy in a day on horseback. Don't know where you'll go from there."

"We'll find our way," said Henan. "We have plenty of time. How'd you hurt your back?"

"I guess I lifted a little too much down at the mine. I don't work there every day, just when they send for me. I hurt it about a week ago and it sure is slow getting better. The pain is way down low in my back. I'm getting behind on my work around here. I took the horse and hauled in some trees about a week before I hurt myself, but that's as far as I got with it. If my back don't get better soon I don't know when I'll get it sawed up and split. It'll be a-get'n cold before you know it. We generally get some frosty mornings in late September."

Henan looked at Calvin before he spoke. "We might saw it up and split it for you afore we go. We got some time."

"I couldn't ask you to do that," Mr. Johnson replied. "I couldn't pay you fer it."

"We wouldn't charge you nuth'n," said Calvin. "Henan and I have lots of experience working in the woods. We could git that firewood split up for you in no time."

"It sure would help me out if you would," said Caleb. "It's been a-worrying me nearly to death."

"We'll work on it in the morning," said Henan. "If'n it takes two days, we'll do it. If'n your wife will feeds us like she do'n this evening, we'll be glad to do the work."

As Henan and Calvin got up to leave, Calvin spotted a banjo sitting in the corner.

"Who plays the banjo?" he asked. It was a crude looking banjo, mostly made of wood.

"I play a little," Caleb Johnson replied.

"Where'd you come by that banjo?" Henan inquired. "Did you make it yourself?"

"No sir, some feller down in Virginia, just below Greenbrier County made it. My dad picked it up somewhere. Dad never could play it much but I got so I could do fairly well. So he gave it to me."

"How about pick'n a tune for us?" Calvin suggested.

Sally Ann handed the banjo to her husband. "Play that *Sandy Boys* for'em, Caleb. I love that tune."

Caleb Johnson placed the banjo comfortably on his lap and played a very clean and hard-driving version of the old mountain tune. He even offered a little vocal a time or two:

*Sixteen miles away from here,*
*Chickens crowin' for day*
*Somebody's upstairs with my true love*
*And he better be getting' away*

*Hey, hey, sandy boys*
*Hey, hey, oh do*
*Hey, hey, Sandy boys,*
*Beware of bugger boo.*

The lyrics brought a big smile to Henan's face and Calvin shook his head from side to side. When he got through singing Caleb played through the first and second part of the tune a couple of more time. He nodded to Sally Ann and she stepped into the middle of the room and showed a pretty good flatfoot dance step. Henan and Caleb smiled from ear to ear as they looked on. They'd never heard the tune but they both loved it. They all shared a good laugh when the tune ended and Henan and Calvin headed for the barn.

As they walked through the barnyard Henan looked at Calvin and smiled. "Did you see her lock her eyes on me when she danced?"

"I saw," Calvin replied.

"Did you notice how her breasts bounced to the beat of that banjo?"

"A man couldn't hardly miss that," Calvin replied.

As they were preparing to bed down for the night Sally Ann appeared in the barn door with a couple of blankets.

"That air is pretty cool this evening," she said. "Looks like there was some cold air coming in behind those storms. I thought you boys might need another blanket. I told Caleb that I would at least offer. He thought it was a good idea. It's uncommonly cool for August, but, of course, you never can tell about August."

Calvin saw that she and Henan had locked eyes and that both of them were looking a little moony eyed on top of that.

"I think I'll go outside and have a smoke," he said. "We appreciate the blankets, Mrs. Johnson."

He walked down by the creek a few yards from the barn and sat down on a rock to roll himself a smoke. Sally Ann was right, he mused, it is going to get chilly tonight. In just a few minutes he saw Sally's lantern heading toward the house. He lit his cigarette and headed back to the barn.

"What happened lover boy? Was she too much for you?"

"I think she lost her nerve. She was sure a-giv'n me the come on but when I started to take holt of her she tuck off for the house."

"Probably a good thing," said Calvin. "I'd hate to see you get yur ass shot off afore we get out of here."

Henan only smiled.

"I'll swanee, Henan, you can't leave the women alone a-tall can you?"

"Me, hell it ain't me that starts it. I don't never start nothin' with a woman, but I'll tell you right now, I ain't gonna turn one down when she throws it at me."

Calvin rarely laughed out loud, but he ended the conversation with a chuckle.

# FIREWOOD AND FIREWORKS

Henan and Calvin were up early the next morning. They peeked out the barn door just before dawn and saw a light in the kitchen of the house. Sally Ann was up and about getting some breakfast, they figured, so they headed up that way, carrying the blankets that she had brought them. She greeted them with a big smile. They sat down to a fine meal of ham, eggs, and a good pan of biscuits. Caleb had not yet gotten up and the door to his room was closed. Calvin noticed that Henan and Sally Ann were still exchanging lingering glances.

"Did Caleb build this house?" Calvin asked. "If'n he did, he sure did a nice job of it."

"No, his dad built this place a few years back. He came up here from Greenbrier County to work in a mill for some of his relatives down close to Fayetteville. He bought this little piece of land and built the house. When Caleb and his brothers were teenagers they worked the farm and helped him build the barn and outbuildings. Then after Caleb and I got married the old man decided he wanted to go back to his old farm in Greenbrier County, so he took off. We moved in here and Caleb has sent his dad some of the money that he makes when he works in the mines. I think he feels guilty about moving into the house without paying no rent."

"Well, hit's a nice place," said Henan. "Looks like you folks have cared for it pretty good."

"We've tried, but I don't know what we'll do if Caleb's back don't get better."

"Speaking of that," said Calvin, "we had better git at that

firewood job, Henan. Don't know if we can finish it in a day or not."

"Oh, I think so," said Henan, "if'n we stay with it and don't loaf around all day."

As is often the case after storms roll through in late summer, it was a beautiful blue-sky morning when they walked out into the woodlot. It appeared that Caleb Johnson had dragged in some red oak trees. He had already cut the limbs off of them. Most of them were a little more than a foot through at the base and were twenty feet or so long. He had constructed a nice little cradle like affair to lay the logs in so they could be sawed off into short sections. Henan and Calvin spent most of the morning with the crosscut saw. They stepped into the house for a minute and checked out the fireplace grate that held the logs. They decided to cut most of the logs into sections that were about three foot long for the fireplace. They sawed some of them pretty short so they could splinter them up for the cook stove.

Calvin saw the two children watching them through the fence. The little boy looked to be about five and he guessed the girl to be about three. Sally Ann brought them some water about ten o'clock and the kids followed along behind her. When the boys sat down on the wood to take a drink, the little girl sat down beside Henan. They seemed to hit it right off and she was soon on his lap. Calvin wasn't surprised because Henan always had a soft spot for kids. Or, he figured old Henan might be trying to impress Sally Ann. But he did not say anything after they all went back to the house.

Henan located a double-bit ax, a pole ax, and a splitting maul with some wedges in one of the sheds. They worked at the splitting process until Sally Ann called them for dinner. Caleb joined them for the meal but he had not made an appearance outside.

"Before you go back to work, I want to show you something," Sally Ann exclaimed.

"Come on down to the cellar with me."

The cellar had been carved out of the hill in back of the house. It was probably eighty percent underground. Sally Ann opened the door and the boys followed her in. The cellar walls were made of cut stone. The stonework impressed them but that was not what impressed them the most.

"Well, for God's sake." said Calvin. "I ain't never seen so much food in one place."

The walls were lined with shelves and each shelf was filled with gleaming jars of canned goods. Green beans, corn, tomatoes, blackberries, peaches, pears, apples, and some things the boys could not identify packed the place. In the back was a large potato bin totally filled with potatoes. In one of the corners there were several wooden crates of sweet potatoes and apples. "Like I told you boys, we ain't got much, but we got a-plenty to eat. So don't feel like you are a-put'n us out by eat'n with us."

"I'd say you're in no danger of starving anytime soon," said Henan. "Folks down whar we come from can stuff too, but I ain't never seen a bounty like this. Whar in the world did you come up with all of them glass jars? I've seen'em before but never that many at one place."

"Caleb's dad brought those up from Greenbrier County. I'm not sure where he got'em, but they sure are handy. That wire fastener harness on top makes them easy to seal. I think some folks call them 'lightning jars' because there so quick to seal. They ain't too common around here and I feel lucky to have'em."

"I'm damned if'n that ain't something," Calvin chimed in.

As was typical with the West Virginia August weather, it got pretty hot by noon. When the boys went back out they both removed their shirts. Swinging the double-bit ax or the splitting maul soon had the sweat pouring from both of them. But they made excellent progress. One of them would split while the other one stacked the pieces in the shed. Then they would change places.

About mid-afternoon they spotted Caleb making his way slowly toward them. He was leaning pretty heavy on a makeshift cane but appeared to be moving a little better.

"Damned if you boys ain't a hell of a team," he said. "I could use you around here full time."

"Hell, you couldn't afford us," said Calvin. "We come pretty high when we're hired out."

"Well, it sure is good of you boys to do this for me. I don't think I would have been able to do it a-tall."

"We just appreciate the hospitality. It sure gave us a good break from the rain and mud," said Henan. "And, we don't mind the work. We've split a bunch of wood in our time."

"I just wish I could afford to pay you something," said Caleb. "But right now, I am just out of money."

"Don't worry yourself none about it," said Calvin. "I think it was a pretty good trade off. If'n you don't care, we might want to spend one more night in your barn. We'll be purty tuckered out by dark and will need a good night's rest afore we take off in the morning."

"You stay as long as you like," said Caleb. "We got plenty to eat around here."

"Yeah, we got a tour of the cellar this morning," said Calvin.

By suppertime, the Fleming boys had all the wood cut, split, and in the shed. They ate so much supper that they felt a little guilty about it. After the meal, Henan apologized a little.

"I guess we ate like a couple of Pole-Chinee hogs," he said. "But we worked up a powerful appetite this afternoon. I ain't worked that hard in a long time. Kinda enjoyed it, really."

"Me too," said Calvin. "I found some muscles in my back that I didn't know was there. I know they are there now cause they are starting to get sore."

"You boys eat all you want," said Sally. "I love to see a hungry man eat. Makes me feel like my cook'n was worth the effort."

Henan and Calvin walked back down to the barn. The sun had gone down. It was a pleasant evening, but again, there was a chill in the air. They sat down on a bench in front of the barn and rolled themselves a cigarette.

"By God, hits pretty chilly for August," said Calvin. "Looks like we might have an early fall a-set'n in."

"Oh, it'll heat up in a few days I 'spect," said Henan. "Sometimes you'll get a cold snap or two in August. But I'd say we'll see some hot days yet. Then agin, I've seen some early September frost a time or two. But there is a chill in the air for shore."

As soon as it got dark, they went into the barn and started to bed down. Sally Ann appeared in the doorway again with the blankets. "It's going to be colder tonight than it was last night," she said, "so I thought I'd bring these back down."

She and Henan were looking right through each other and Calvin figured there was going to be some fireworks this time. So he excused himself again. This time he walked over to the woodshed and admired their work as he had another smoke. He didn't see Sally Ann's lantern for about thirty minutes. Finally, he saw her making her way to the house. Henan was bedded down when he went into the barn.

"Was she a little easier to handle this evening?" asked Calvin.

"Ain't nobody will ever know that cept'n me and Sally Ann." Henan replied as he rolled over to go to sleep.

When Sally Ann went into her bedroom, Caleb was still awake and was propped up in the bed.

"What you been do'en so long?" he inquired.

"Those are such nice boys," she said. "I just enjoyed sitting and talking with them for a while."

"They are nice fellers," Caleb responded, "and damned good workers too."

Next morning Calvin and Henan enjoyed their last meal with the Johnson family. The meal consisted of something akin to a pancake. Sally Ann called them Ho Cakes. The basic ingredient appeared to be corn meal. The cakes were topped with cow butter and some maple syrup that Caleb and Sally Ann had made back in February.

"We used this stuff only for special occasions," said Sally. "It takes an awful pile of sugar maple sap to come up with a quart of it. We made three quarts. They ain't a powerful lot of sugar maples hereabouts. They say more of them grow up in the higher mountains."

"I think some folks down our way make some but I ain't never tasted it," said Henan. "But it's mighty good. It's a shame it's so hard to get."

"My dad always said that really good stuff is always hard to get," Sally said with a broad smile.

Calvin looked at Henan for a reaction, but he didn't see one.

As the boys saddled up and prepared to take off, Sally Ann came out with a couple of pieces of cornbread and some hog meat in a little package. "You might get hungry afore you get to Summersville," she said.

"Thanks," said Calvin. "We're might grateful for your hospitality."

"If you boys come by this way again you'll always be welcome," she said with about the prettiest smile that Henan had ever seen.

"You can depend on it," he said.

## SUMMERSVILLE DIVERSION

The road had dried up in most places as the Fleming boys made their way toward Summersville. They were making much better time than they had at any other time on their journey. Henan and Calvin rode tall in their saddles into Summersville during the mid-morning hours. It looked to be a thriving little town with several stores and businesses. The county government was housed in a two-story frame building that appeared to have been a dwelling at one time. They later learned that a new courthouse was under construction. There were several restaurants and a couple of inns. They also noticed a rather large blacksmith shop and stable.

They discussed where they might stop and inquire about the best way to get to Boggs. Since they were officially fugitives from justice, the boys decided not to stop by the little courthouse and ask for directions. Henan thought it might be interesting to know if their reputation had spread this far north, but he figured they might get into more than they bargained for in the courthouse.

"I 'spect we might get some good directions in the courthouse, but we are also liable to find our picture up on the wall. You just never know what the law down in Wise County might have done."

"I agree," Calvin replied. "Maybe we ought to go back to that blacksmith shop and stable we passed coming in."

As the boys made their way in that direction they noticed a crowd of people off on one of the side streets. They could hear loud talking and laughter.

"Let's see what's go'n over thar." Calvin suggested.

They rode over toward the crowd and noticed a sign that said *THE GREAT RICOTTELLI. Who can throw him off his feet? Everyone welcome to try for $2.00.*

They dismounted, tied their horses, and walked over to where the crowd was gathered. There was a one dollar fee to get inside the roped off area. Such events were fairly common in small mountain towns.

A small boxing type ring had been erected in the street and a man in a suit and tie was speaking to the crowd. "Anyone who can take the Great Ricottelli off his feet in three minutes or less can take home $50.00. Of course, if he puts you down first, you lose." Ricottelli was standing in the ring looking the crowd over. He was a massive man, looked to be about six foot three or four and Henan figured he weighed close to two hundred and fifty pounds. He had powerful looking shoulders and a wide bull neck.

The man in the suit kept talking. "This match is based on the old Scots-Irish tradition of wrestling. There is no need to hold the opponent down. Once you take a man off his feet and he hits the ground, the match is over. We will modify the rules just a bit in that both Ricottelli and the opponent can also use their fists to knock their opponent down. No holds are barred."

Calvin and Henan studied the big Italian for a few minutes. "I might want to try him a round," said Calvin. "That would be an easy $50.00."

"You better think about that, Calvin," Henan suggested. "He looks to me like he would be a hard man to get off'n his feet."

Two men had already paid their fee and were waiting to get in the ring.

"Let's watch a couple of them and see how it goes," said Calvin.

The first opponent was nearly as big as Ricottelli but he was not as muscular. The two men moved slowly out into the center of the ring and circled each other a few times. It was over in an instant. When the man stepped forward to get into a wrestling hold, Ricottelli got a hammerlock around his neck and threw him quickly to the mat. The crowd moaned.

The second opponent was a smaller man but looked tough and wiry. He too circled Ricottelli a few times then attempted to dive for his knees in a tackling motion. The agile Italian stepped back and avoided the move and the man fell to one knee. Ricottelli pushed him over and the match ended.

"I think I can take him down," said Calvin. "I want to talk to that feller in the suit afore I try though."

Henan smiled. "If'n you get in thar you'd better be mighty careful. A man like that could hurt you."

"We'll see," Calvin replied.

"I have a couple of questions," Calvin said to the man in the suit. "You say there's no holds barred. Is that right?"

"That's correct," the man answered. "Any way you can put him on the canvas is fair."

Calvin was not a big man. He was around five feet ten inches tall and weighed in at about 175 pounds. But he was tough as they come and quick as a cat. He had been in some brawls in his time.

"I think I'll try him a shot," Calvin said to the man as he handed him the two-dollar entry fee. He sat down on the ground and removed his shoes. Then he stood up and took off his shirt. He gave The Great Ricottelli one more long look before he climbed into the ring. Ricottelli backed into one corner and Calvin took the opposite corner. There was no bell. The man in the suit just yelled, "go."

Calvin allowed the big Italian to take two or three steps before he moved. He then charged out of his corner like a banshee. He ran toward Ricottelli as fast as he could and as he approached he jumped high into the air and struck the big man in the chest with both his feet with all of the force he had in him. Ricottelli was totally caught by surprise and fell backwards. He attempted to catch himself on the ropes but both knees hit the canvas. Calvin, who had landed on his feet, barreled into Ricottelli with a blocking motion and rolled him over on his back. The crowd went crazy. Calvin smiled and waved at the crowd and got out of the ring as fast as he could.

Henan walked up to him as he was putting his shoes back on and patted him on the head. "You cleaned his clock, Calvin. No doubt about it."

The man in the suit came over shaking his head and gave Calvin a fifty-dollar bill.

"Easiest fifty bucks I ever earned," said Calvin as they remounted their horses.

They rode slowly back up the street and found the blacksmith working at an anvil outside the shop. They approached the heavy built man who sported a short but very dark beard. When he saw them approach, he looked up and smiled. "What can I do for you gentlemen?" he asked pleasantly.

"We are look'n for some help in finding a place called Boggs," Henan ventured. "We have family there and have come up from down in Virginia to visit."

"What part of the great state of Virginia do you a hail from?" the man inquired.

"From the central part." Henan lied. "We're rural folks, not close to any town to amount to anything,"

He again figured there was no use advertising where they were really from in case anyone ever came looking for them. He also decided right then on the spot that they probably should not use their own names from this day forward.

"Well, actually, you boys are pretty close to Boggs. But there is one big obstacle in the way. You will have to cross Powell's Mountain in order to get over to Birch River. But once you get on the other side, you'll see the Birch. Then you can just follow that river a few miles up to Boggs. Just at the foot of Powell's Mountain, on the other side, you'll come to a little place known as Birch Village. I'm sure someone there can point you up the river to Boggs. Powell's Mountain is steep and rough in some places so it will be slow going."

"We ain't no strangers to mountains," said Calvin. "We'll handle that OK."

"Also ought to warn you," the man continued, "the mountain is noted for being infested with rattlesnakes. I 'spect their still active up there this time of year."

"We ain't afeerd of them," said Henan. "We used to go shoot'n rattlesnakes for sport."

"Well, sounds like you boys will be fine. I hope you have a pleasant journey to Boggs. You should be able to get there before dark."

"We certainly obliged to you," said Henan.

## ARRIVING IN BOGGS

The boys decided to stop at the foot of Powell's Mountain and eat the cornbread and pork that Sally Ann had given them. They pulled up in the shade of a big red oak tree and dismounted. The cool spell appeared to be over. The sun was hot.

"Maybe this will keep us a-go'n until we get to sis's house," said Calvin. "I hope she has something to eat when we get thar."

"Well, she told us to come and stay as long as we wanted so I guess she's a-figure'n on feed'n us something. Course, she won't have no idy when were a-com'n."

The ride over the mountain was not uneventful. The boys hadn't made it halfway up the south side of Powell when a big rattler spooked Henan's horse. The horse jumped sideways to avoid the snake and Henan hit the ground but he held on to the reins. Calvin did not even hesitate. He pulled the .44 from his shoulder holster and nailed the rattler with one shot.

"That's one time I was glad that you are a better shot than me," said Henan. "I'd a never hit that son-of-a-bitch like you did."

"That old snake never had a chance," said Calvin. "I'm just glad he missed your horse. I saw him just about the time your horse bucked."

"He's a big'n," said Henan. "He'd have done some damage fer shore."

The road over the mountain was in decent shape for the most part but there were some long, drawn-out mudholes in a few sections that they had to pick their way around. But they generally made good time. As they neared the bottom they could see a few buildings scattered along a river.

"I guess that must be what the blacksmith called Birch Village," said Henan. "Ain't much thar, I can see that already."

"No, but it looks like a right purty river rolling along behind it though." Calvin replied. "Guess that must be the Birch."

Birch Village consisted of a few houses, a post office, and what looked to be a combination sawmill and gristmill. There was also a country store. They tied their mounts in front of the store and went in and asked directions. The store was empty except for the man behind the counter.

"Hello," ventured Henan. "We're strangers in this neck of the woods and was wonder'n if'n you could give us a little help."

"I'll certainly give it a try," the man replied. "What can I do for you?"

"We're looking for a place called Boggs," said Henan. "We are told that hits not far from this village."

"You've been told right," the man replied. "You are within about five or six miles of it. You just follow the road right up the river and you will come to Boggs. It ain't much of a road, not hardly passable by wagon most of the time, but you will do fine on your horses. You will cross Skyles Creek before you get to Boggs. That's the only obstacle in your way. Fording the creek will be no problem because the creeks are all pretty low this time of year. Even though we've had some pretty good rain showers, that creek runs out fast."

"You wouldn't happen to know a feller by the name of Thomas who lives up that way would you?" Henan continued.

"Would that be Ralph Thomas?" the man inquired.

"That's the man," Henan replied.

"I know just where he lives," the storekeeper said with a smile. "He's got a little spread up there right before you get to the post office at Boggs. I think he works some at a sawmill up at Skyles and he also raises a few horses. You'll notice the house sett'n back in a little holler. It's a log house with an addition built on. There's also a good-sized barn down beside the creek. More than likely, you'll see a couple of horses grazing in the field."

"That would be him all right," said Henan. "We are much obliged to you."

The Fleming brothers were impressed with the countryside as they made their way up the Birch River. The river itself was quite pretty but they were most impressed with the broad bottoms, especially those on the left side of the river. Some of the bottoms were cleared and were being used as pasture fields. The August grass was still green, probably because there had been some rain. They came to Skyles Creek just as the man at the store had told them they would. It was a shallow creek, which they had to ford. It wasn't long until they spotted the house and rode their horses up into the barn lot. As they approached the house, their brother-in-law met them in the yard. It was August 17th.

"Been expecting you boys," he said unenthusiastically. "In fact, I was beginning to worry that you might have got waylaid some where along the way."

"No nothing like that," said Calvin. "We just took our time. We were'nt in no hurry to get here. We were just in one hell of a hurry to get out of Wise County."

"I can understand that," Ralph replied. "What in the world is going on down there anyway?"

Henan thought a minute before he answered.

"Well, some of'em down thar are trying to mix me and Calvin up in the big shoot'n that happened up at Pound Gap. You know they have old Doc Taylor in jail, waiting to be hanged. He's been convicted. They have a $700.00 reward out for us, even though we didn't have a damned thing to do with it. I think Cap Hall is behind it. You know that son-of-a-bitch don't you?"

"Don't really know him but I have certainly heard enough about him. I'd say you boys made a good move getting out of there, at least till things blow over a little."

"Hit don't look like hits ever gonna blow over. They ain't no way we'd ever get a fair trial down thar now. We all know that. We've been lay'n low back in the mountains up close to the Kentucky line, but we was about to run out of places to hide. That's why we wrote to you."

"Well, you're welcome to stay here till you can get yourselves established. The sister and I are doing pretty good here."

"We'll be glad to pay you some board," said Henan. "We wouldn't want to put you out none."

"We can talk about that once you get yourselves established," he replied. "I think your sis has fixed up a couple of bunks back in the addition so you'll have somewhere to lay your head."

"One more thing," said Calvin. "Whilst we're here we are going to go by another name, just to be safe. From now on, we will go by Walt and Frank Johnson. That's what we'll use to get our mail."

"That's a good idea," Ralph replied.

## GOING STRAIGHT IN BOGGS

While Henan and Calvin still had some money to spare, they decided that they needed to find some kind of work so they could move out of the Thomas home and get a place of their own. Henan was very keen on getting Catherine to come up and get settled with him. During the third morning after their arrival they raised the question with their host. Henan also wrote a short letter to his wife informing her that they had arrived in Boggs and that he would be sending some money soon. He also told her to use the Johnson name when she replied. They rode down to the post office that morning and mailed it. When he got back to the house he asked Ralph about getting a job.

"Do you know where a man might pick up some work around here?" Henan asked Ralph. "Me and Cal need to go to work. I kinda like the looks of this country. It looks like a place I could settle. These big wide bottoms along the river make it look invit'n. As you know, down where we come from there ain't much bottomland. The mountains are high and steep. They run right down into the rivers and creeks. If'n we could find a way to make a living, we might just stick around up here. We noticed as we traveled up from Bluefield, folks know how to make a living. We saw the tail end of some fine gardens and enjoyed some mighty fine meals along the way. All the folks were nice and friendly."

"Well there are some sawmills around and there's some timber cutt'n go'n on. Can you boys do that kind of work?"

"I'd say we can," said Calvin. "We've done some of it down home."

"I know a feller up on the Beard Fork of Beaver Creek who might be looking for some help. That's up near a place called Tioga. He's got one of those portable steam powered sawmills. He's been sawing some timber for about six months. He also has a good-sized farm. I'd guess he wants help at both the mill and the farm. Now it's a good little piece up there but you could probably ride it from here, or else he might have a place to put you up. I ain't sure about that. His name is William Roberts. I'm acquainted with him but don't know him all that well. Seems like a good feller, though. If you boys are interested in that, I'll ride up there with you in a couple of days. I'm gonna be busy tomorree and the next day."

On September 3rd, the three men rode up to the William Roberts place to inquire about work. Mr. Roberts had a pretty nice spread with several head of livestock. They could see the sawmill in the bottom below his house. It was located close to the creek and was snuggled up against a little bank. It did not look like there had been any activity there recently but there was a pile of logs beside it. They spotted Mr. Roberts out near his barn and rode up toward him.

"Good morning, Mr. Roberts," Ralph said as he got off his horse.

Mr. Roberts looked him over before he spoke. "You're Ralph Thomas ain't you?"

"That's right," Ralph replied. "I got a couple of relatives here who are looking for work. You got anything going on?"

"Well, as you can see, I've got a bunch of logs down by the mill to saw up. They've been a-laying down there for a month or more. Haven't been able to find anyone to help me. And, I have plenty of chores around the farm here that needs to be done, got a bunch of fence that needs to be built. You boys know how to run a sawmill?"

"We ain't sawyers or noth'n like that," said Calvin, "but we have both worked around mills some."

"I can do the saw'n," said Mr. Roberts, "but it's just a hard job to do it all by yourself. If you boys can do that kind of work, I sure could use you. How about you, Ralph? You a-want'n work too?"

"No, I got a job and plenty to do at my own place," said Ralph.

"Just trying to help these boys get settled. Don't suppose you could board them, could you?"

"Not full time," said Mr. Roberts, "but they could stay here some if we have a heavy workload."

"That ought to work out fine," Ralph replied. "They can stay with me when they need to."

"I got one more question," said Henan. "How in the world did you ever get that mill up this holler. Hit don't look very portable to me."

"The mill came in four pieces. It came into Flatwoods by rail and I hauled it in here in two wagons. It was a chore I don't mind telling you. I can also tell you that I ain't planning to move it anywhere, portable or not. I think she'll stay right where she's a-sett'n. It cost me a lot of money, but I can sell the boards as fast as I can get them sawed up, so it'll soon pay for itself. The hardest part is getting the logs in here and getting them on the carrier that moves them toward the saw."

"Well, I hope me and Calvin will be of some help to you," said Henan.

That very day the Fleming boys started working. Their first job was to help Mr. Roberts saw up the big pile of logs by his sawmill. It was mostly white and red oak. The logs were of different lengths and the first order of business was to size them and get them ready to be moved up onto the mill itself. It was backbreaking work wrestling the logs into position to be sawed. Most of them had to be pulled closer to the mill with a team of horses, and then rolled up onto the platform beside the mill. When the logs were hauled in they were deposited on the little bank above the mill. That made it easier to get the logs onto the carrier.

It did not take Mr. Roberts long to figure out that the Fleming boys were quite capable. He really like Henan and was pleased to have both of them. A strong personal relationship developed between Mr. Roberts and Henan. Henan did have a way about him that made folks like him right off. Mr. Roberts paid them at the end of the first week and told them that he would be glad to have them to come work for him full time.

As it turned out, they did not work every day, but they worked enough to make a little money. Just as Henan promised, he began sending his wife money through the mail and told her in each letter that he was trying to find a way to bring her up to Boggs.

Henan and Calvin were model citizens while in the Birch River area. Even though there was plenty of moonshine whiskey in the area, neither of them had taken a drink since they left Virginia. Nor did they make any attempt to get involved in the sale of it. They did not socialize much but they always went down to the post office every Saturday afternoon to check the mail and to pick up a few supplies in the small store in the post office building.

There was generally several locals who loafed at the store on Saturday so the boys got to know some of them. Both Henan and Calvin enjoyed listening to the conversations at the store. They got a real kick out of a man by the name of Barnette, a grizzled old timer who liked to tell stories. One evening while the boys were sitting on a bench outside the store Mr. Barnette stopped by and joined them. After a long stare at both of them he started his conversation with a question. "Airy one of you boys ever saw the ocean?" he asked.

"No, can't say as we have," Calvin replied.

"I saw it one time," Mr. Barnette continued. "I used to live down in Highland County, Virginia. Me and two other boys rode our horses over to the coast to look at it. We was twenty-one at the time. It took us four days to ride it. When we came out to where we could see it, we were on a rocky place. It's a sight to see, I'll tell'ya."

"Did you get in it?" Henan inquired.

"No, we didn't get in it", said Mr. Barnette. "We talked to a feller who lived there and he said there were creatures in there called jellyfish that would sting the hell out of you. So we didn't risk it. But we saw the ocean."

"I believe that if I rode that far I would have at least stuck my toe in it," said Calvin.

"Well, when we got back home we sorta wished we had, but we never done it," Mr. Barnette concluded.

Henan and Calvin just chuckled.

By the middle of September the boys had settled into a routine. They felt pretty safe in Boggs. But during the first week of November, Henan got a disturbing letter from his wife, informing him that Marshall (Doc) Taylor had been hanged. As Henan read the lines he felt a tightening in his throat and a slight chill ran down his spine. She also said that Cap Hall was bound and determined to find him and Calvin. Henan was comforted somewhat in that his wife said that at this point in time they were still looking for them in the local area. She had attended the Doc Taylor hanging and described the scene.

# THE HANGING OF MARSHAL (DOC) TAYLOR
## (Wise, Virginia, October 27, 1893)

Catherine reported that Marshall Doc Taylor had been brought before the court on September 9, 1893, and sentenced to be hanged. She said that during the trial Doc had quoted long passages of scripture. He also warned the court that he had talked with Christ and Christ had told him that he would rise from the dead. He further told them that Christ himself would bring punishment upon those who had persecuted him. But none of this appeared to have had any influence on the judge.

His lawyers also made an attempt to have Doc declared insane and to avert the sentencing, but the motion never got anywhere. Catherine said that some of his friends had tried to circulate a petition, which they wanted to forward to the governor asking that Doc be declared insane. They were asking for a life sentence instead of execution. But the petition got very few signatures. The execution was set for October 27.

According to Catherine's account of the hanging, Doc Taylor had requested permission to preach his own funeral before he was hanged. His request was granted. Twenty-five heavily armed men guarded him the night before the execution and also during his rant before the large crowd that had gathered. She said that Doc talked for about an hour and a half.

It was reported by some of those in attendance that Doc had been allowed to drink wine all morning to help him sustain his courage. So when he took to his "pulpit" he was heavily under the influence.

He warned the crowd to stay away from evil doings lest they end up the same way that he did. But he assured them that he had made all of his confessions to Jesus Christ and that he was certain that he was right with God. His salvation was assured, he exclaimed.

After his lengthy sermon Doc was escorted back to jail. Witnesses said that he spent most of the time reading the Bible, and that he made a final prayer before he was taken toward the scaffold. As he approached the scaffold he was dressed in a white suit his wife had made for the occasion. She had also made him a white hood to cover his head. Just before the hanging, the sheriff put the white hood over his head. Catherine said she did not have a very good view from where she was standing but some of those close to the scaffold said that Doc lost his nerve at the final moment of truth and crumpled to the floor. He had to be pulled back up so the rope could be adjusted around his neck. She said she could see his head and shoulders at the moment of his hanging.

The trap door was sprung at 2:20 p.m. and Doc was pronounced dead by a physician eighteen minutes later. His body was given over to his family for burial.

But the most disturbing part of Catherine's letter was the part that told about the talk that a big effort was going to be made to capture the Fleming brothers.

She said that there were all kinds of wild rumors about the boys being "nearly captured" but they had always escaped. Several people were still reporting that they had seen Calvin and Henan in the area. There are, of course, always a lot of sightings when criminals are at large.

One of the local papers had reported that the Fleming brothers were believed to be hiding out deep in the Virginia or Kentucky mountains and they, "were a menace to the well-being of the local citizens."

The letter disturbed Henan and Calvin but they were again somewhat comforted by the fact that no one down around Wise County had yet figured out where they were.

She closed her letter by saying that Cap Hall was bound and determined to get the Fleming boys, one way or another.

(*Endnote*: Marshall Taylor told the crowd at the hanging that he might arise in three days, but he failed to do so.)

# THE WISE COUNTY POSSE

During the trial and conviction of Marshall Taylor for the Ira
Mullins massacre, there was much testimony that implicated Henan
and Calvin. Witnesses testified that Henan and Calvin had been seen
in the presence of Marshall Taylor the evening before the shooting
at Pound Gap. One witness testified that he saw them riding tall
in their saddles and all of them were carrying rifles. Plus, the lone
survivor of the Pound Gap massacre had said all along that even
though she had not gotten a good look at their faces, she was pretty
sure that Henan and Calvin were the other two shooters at Pound
Gap on that fateful day.

Reward money had been posted for the Fleming brothers long
before the conviction and execution of Marshall Taylor. The total
for the capture of the two men had reached $700.00, a respectable
sum of money in 1893. So the search for them continued even after
Taylor had been executed.

Three Wise County residents, Ed Hall, John Branham, and E.J.
(Doc) Swindall were determined to bring the Fleming boys to justice.
Like Wyatt Earp, hero of the big shootout at the OK Coral, Ed Hall
was not exactly a Sunday school teacher. While he was interested in
the reward, he also carried a personal grudge against the Fleming
brothers. In addition, Doc had a widespread reputation for violence.
He was most definitely the force behind the posse.

In order to make things legal and proper Hall managed to get the
three of them deputized. To begin their search, Hall bribed a postal
worker to intercept any letters that came into the area that were

addressed to Catherine, or to any of the other identifiable members of the Fleming clan. It wasn't long until a letter was intercepted that revealed the location of Henan and Calvin. They were working in a timber and lumber operation up on the Birch River in Webster County. Nearly two years after the Pound Gap massacre, the posse got its provisions together and set out for West Virginia.

They began their journey in January of 1894 and it was cold, very cold. Following the same route that Marshall Taylor used when he attempted to escape, and the same route that the Fleming boys used when they successfully fled the area, the posse caught the train in Norton for Bluefield. But, unlike the Fleming boys, they paid the fare and did not hop a freight. When they got to Bluefield, they also learned that there was no rail transportation that would take them any closer to Birch River without going two or three hundred miles out of their way. But unlike Henan and Calvin, they decided to walk to their destination. They struck out for Beckley on a very cold January morning. Ed Hall was the self-proclaimed leader of the posse and he was calling the shots on the routes and methods of travel.

"I'm not sure where the hell we are going," he remarked as they headed north, "but I think we are all plenty tough enough to handle whatever comes along."

"I hope you're right," Doc Swindall chimed in, "because this wind we're facing is coming right out of the North Pole."

There was no snow cover but a fine snow was blowing. It was the kind of snow pellets that bit your face when you walked into it. The posse was expecting cold weather so they were all dressed warmly, or as warmly as they knew how. The three men did not present a very good image. Ed (Cap) Hall was a stocky man, rarely shaved and had an air about him that almost immediately turned people off. He wore his dark hair shoulder length. John Branham was leaner and had a more pleasant demeanor about him, but he was a quiet man when he was among strangers, not the kind that would engage strangers in conversation. He kept his face shaved most of the time but also wore his hair long. Doc Swindall was probably the best looking of the three. His hair was lighter in color and he kept it short. He was a man of average build but his shoulders were especially broad for a man who was relatively small in stature. He was also a complainer and wasn't as tough as the other two members of the posse.

"How long is it going to take to walk to Boggs?" John Branham asked as he thrust his chin forward.

"I ain't got no damned idy," Ed hall replied, "but I'd say we ain't gonna walk it in a day. That's for sure."

"Where the hell we gonna stay at night?" Swindall asked. "It's too damned cold to sleep outside, or at least it is fer me."

"Well, I blieve that we can surely find some folks along the way that'll put us up, especially if we tell them that we are deputies on the way to arrest some dangerous criminals."

But Doc Swindall was not too happy with that response. "Hell's fire," he said, "I doubt seriously if folks who don't know us from Adam are gonna let us inside their houses. I ain't too crazy about sleeping in somebody's barn in this kind of weather. We ain't gone more'n eight or ten miles and I'm already froze stiff."

"Oh, shit, Doc, you're tougher than that. We'll be OK. We'll find some folks that will let us sleep on the floor or maybe hang us from the rafters!"

Doc Swindall did not honor Ed Halls attempt at humor with a response. He just kept trudging forward. John Branham didn't have much to say about their predicament. He just fed himself a big chaw of tobacco and kept walking.

As the sun dropped over the southwestern ridge, the clouds began to thicken and the snow turned to flakes. The temperature appeared to be rising slightly and the wind died down some.

"It looks like the snow might be set'n in," Cap Hall announced. "We might oughta start looking for a place to roost."

"I ain't seen a house for the past two miles," Doc Swindall replied. "Ain't nobody lives up here."

"One will turn up pretty soon," Cap replied. "We'll just keep trudging for a while."

It wasn't long until they spotted a spread on the right hand side of the road. It looked to be a small house with some outbuildings. The posse made its way up the slight grade that led to the house and Cap Hall knocked on the door.

A man with shoulder length hair and a long beard responded to the knock.

"Good evening," Cap ventured. "We are a deputized posse from down in Wise County, trying to make our way to Webster County. We're a-looking for a place where we might spend the night. Would you have some place where we might rest for the night?"

The bearded man gave them a good long stare, and then looked them over from head to foot. "From down in Virginy, aire you?"

"Yessir, down in Wise County. We are on the trail of a couple of killers who some folks told us are hiding out up on the Birch River."

"Step in out of the cold so's I can close the door," the homeowner replied.

They all stepped inside and Cap Hall stuck out his hand but he got no response.

"As you can see," the man said, "this is an awful small house and I ain't got no place to put you where you could lie down. Now I got a blacksmith shop out back here where you could build you up a coal fire and maybe sleep on the floor. That forge fire will warm that building up pretty nice. You could sleep out there, I reckon, or at least get out of the weather for the night."

"We'd be much obliged," said Cap. "We have our own blankets."

The bearded, rather unfriendly man went out to the building with them and helped them get the forge going. "You can stay here if you want. It's all I got to offer," he said as he left them alone.

"Not a very friendly son-of-a-bitch, is he?" said John Branham. "Guess you noticed that he didn't offer us anything to eat or noth'n like that."

"Yeah, I noticed that," Doc Swindall replied. "I didn't see no woman around, did you?"

"Nary a one," Cap Hall responded. "But there was another room off to the side. Guess she could have been hide'n in there."

The blacksmith shop did not have a floor but it did appear to be a dried-in building. The blacksmith forge did warm the little building up fairly well when the coal caught up and started putting out some heat. Each of them found a space where they could halfway lie down and rest up against the wall. It was a tough night for them but they stayed reasonably warm. They got up just after dawn. Cap Hall opened the door and reported that there was just a skiff of snow. They ate a little bit of jerky and some stale bread that they had purchased in Bluefield and left without saying anything to the owner.

"We'll be just as friendly as he was," said Cap Hall. "I'm surprised the asshole even offered the building."

"Well, he at least did that," said Doc. "He could have thrown our ass out in the cold. I wonder how far it is to the town they called Beckley. I sure could use a good meal."

"From what some of them said down at Bluefield, hits a pretty good hike yet," said Doc. "One of 'em said it was about forty miles, and I'd say we ain't walked more than half of that. We ain't got much daylight this time 'o year. We need to get a move on. I'd say we'd git there some time today."

The sun broke through the clouds about ten o'clock and it warmed the air a little. The three men set a pretty fast pace and arrived in Beckley during the late afternoon. The sun had not yet gone down. They stopped at a restaurant and enjoyed a meal about four o'clock.

"Accord'n to what one of them fellers in the restaurant told me, we've still got a hell of a long walk ahead of us," said Doc Swindall. "He said we are looking at two or three days at least. I think we had better hole up here tonight and get us a good night's sleep in a warm place."

"Sounds like a good idea to me," John Branham replied. "I ain't looking forward to sleeping in another blacksmith shed."

"Neither am I," Doc Swindall added.

Cap Hall was reluctant to go along with the suggestion but finally caved in.

"I guess it might be good to get a fresh start but I want to make damned sure I get to Boggs before those Fleming boys find out we are on their trail. Someone down in Wise County will probably write to them."

"If this Boggs place is as far out of the way as everyone says it is, I don't know how the hell the mail ever gets there," Doc Swindall replied.

The posse spent the night in a boarding house, of sorts. It was a large room filled with cots. But it was a warm place, and probably because January did not bring out many travelers, it was not crowded. All three of them slept well and enjoyed a good breakfast the next morning. They were on their way by about eight o'clock the next morning. There was still some snow on the ground and the wind had picked up again. It was cold. According to what they were told, they would first come to a village called Oak Hill. The next settlement would be Fayetteville. They should be able to make it to Fayetteville in a day if they set a fast pace. Just east of Fayetteville they would find a walking trail over the hill to where they could pick up the Weston-Gauley Bridge Turnpike. The Turnpike would take them to Summersville in Nicholas County. From there they would have to get some more directions.

# A MUCH NEEDED WELCOME MAT

The Wise County Posse walked into Oak Hill around noon. The wind was still blowing and it was bitter cold. The ground was frozen solid so they had no mud to contend with. They found a place to eat and had a good meal. Doc Swindall suggested that they have one more cup of coffee before they left because he was in no hurry to go back out into the cold wind. But Cap Hall decided to press ahead and walk on through Fayetteville before nightfall.

"We ain't got all damned year to get this done," he said. "I keep worrying that them Fleming boys will git word that we are coming afore we git thar. If'n they do they'll hightail it out of there. If they do we may never catch'em."

"We'll catch their ass," John Branham boasted, "if'n we have to go to Philadelphia."

"Cap," said Doc Swindall, "have you give any thought to how we are going to git them back to Wise County oncet we catch'em?"

"I've thought about it some," Cap Hall replied. "We'll keep their hands tied and make'em walk in front of us while we're moving. At night we can tie'em up and one of us will have to stay awake."

"If'n hits as cold on the way back as it is now, I don't know where the hell we're going to stay at night," said Doc. "Ain't nobody gonna want to put up with criminals in their house or barn."

"Stop worrying about it, Doc," said Cap Hall. "It may be that we won't have to take'em back alive anyway."

"But what's that do to the reward?" asked John Branham. "They ain't wanted dead or alive are they?"

64

"Let's worry about that when the time comes," said Cap Hall as he trudged onward.

The posse walked through Fayetteville without stopping and found the narrow road that led across the mountain to Gauley Bridge. Cap had in his mind that they might make it all the way to the Weston-Gauley Bridge Turnpike before dark. But as the evening started to close in on them, he changed his mind. He decided that it might be a good idea to find a warm place to stay before they went too much farther.

When they were about halfway up the mountain, Cap spotted a homestead sitting back in a little cove. It was a pretty little spot with a fairly good-looking house on it. The house looked to be a bit larger than the one where they stayed with the unfriendly man. Cap Hall walked up and boldly knocked on the door. A pleasant looking man, appearing to be forty years old or so, answered the knock.

"Good evening, gentlemen," he said with a half smile. "What can I do for you on this cold evening."

"Well," said Cap Hall, "we're a-looking for a warm place to spend the night. We got a long walk ahead of us."

"Is that so?" said the man as he invited them inside. "Where are you headed?"

Cap Hall went into a long description of their trip and explained that they were lawmen on the trail of some mean killers who had escaped from Wise County.

"We have good reasons to believe that they are staying in Boggs," said Cap.

"I've heard of that place," the man answered. "I am a teacher but also work some at sawmilling. I've been told there is some millwork up that way. By the way, my name is Caleb McHenry and this is my wife Carrie," he continued as he extended his hand to all three members of the posse and nodded to his wife who was standing by the fire. "Do you have credentials?"

"I have this letter here from the Wise County Courthouse authorizing us to arrest these men," said Cap, as he pulled the letter from his jacket pocket. When he pulled his jacket back the host saw the big .44 caliber pistol nestled against Cap's shoulder.

"What have these men done?" Caleb McHenry asked.

"They helped shoot six people down in cold blood," said Doc Swindall. "It was an ambush."

"Is that so?" said Caleb McHenry. "It sounds like you boys are on a right good mission. Me and the woman will be glad to put you up for the night. There is only the two of us and we have some room here inside the house. There's a room through the door yonder that has a bed. Two of you can sleep in the bed and Carrie will fix a pallet on the floor for the other one. Have you had your supper?"

"We're not really hungry. We ate a pretty good meal in Oak Hill," Cap Hall replied.

Carrie McHenry spoke for the first time. "I have some left over corn dodger," she said. "I can give you some of that with some sweet milk if you'd just like a bite of something."

"That would be awful nice," said the always-hungry Doc Swindall.

They all sat around the crude table that was located in front of the fireplace and enjoyed an hour or so of conversation and corn dodger. Finally, Caleb McHenry pushed his chair back and said, "we turn in pretty early here on the mountain and I figure you men are tired also. We always have a scripture reading and a prayer before we go to bed. I hope you boys will join us. Are you boys men of God?"

None of the members of the posse had been inside of a church since they were children, but, taking their cue from Cap Hall, they all shook their heads in the affirmative.

Caleb McHenry gave them a skeptical look but thumbed through his Bible until he came to Ecclesiastes. "In view of what you boys have told me, I think we can find some appropriate words from the preacher."

"This is the King James Version," he said, "and we will begin with the first few verses of Chapter I." He began reading.

*The words of the Preacher, the son of David, King of Jerusalem.*
*Vanity of vanities, saith the preacher; all is vanity. What profit hath*
*a man of all his labors which he taketh under the sun. One*
*generation passes away, and another generation cometh; but the*
*earth abideth forever.*

Then Caleb McHenry skipped to verse 9.

*The thing that hath been, it is that which shall be; and that which*
*is done is that which shall be done; and there is no new thing*
*under the sun.*

He then looked at the three men from Virginia and said sternly.
"Those are very wise words. Men often come to think that there is
no one quite like them and that they have done deeds that have never
been done. They are kidding themselves. There is nothing special
about any of us."

He then skipped to the Third Chapter;

*To everything there is a season, and a time to every person under*
*the Heaven. A time to be born and a time to die; a time to plant*
*and a time to pluck up that which is planted. A time to kill, and a*
*time to heal; a time to break down, and a time to build up.*

"I sincerely hope that when you gentlemen come face to face with
the men you are after that you consider the words of the preacher. I
hope you will consider that while there is a time to kill, this may be
the time to heal, and to show mercy towards these criminals, however
evil they may be, and take them back to the justice rendered by their
peers."

Caleb McHenry and his wife, Carrie, then knelt down on their
knees to pray. The Virginia men uncomfortably joined them.

"Dear Lord we thank you for all of the blessings that you have
bestowed upon. We thank you for lending us the land that we dwell

on. We thank you for helping us grow the crops that we bring to our table to nourish us. And, Lord, be with these good men from Virginia as they go forth to right the wrongs that have been committed. Lead, guide and direct them to do the right thing. We ask these things in the name of your son, Jesus Christ. Amen."

With that said they all arose and Caleb shook each man's hand before they retired.

The Virginia posse went silently to the place that had been prepared for them.

# THE WESTON-GAULEY BRIDGE TURNPIKE

The Wise County posse was awakened the next morning by sounds from the kitchen. They heard the rattle of the cook stove burners and the banging of iron skillets. As the men stirred around and begin lacing up their boots they got a whiff of coffee brewing.

When they walked out into the living area they noticed that the table had already been set and Carrie McHenry was busy at the stove.

"You boys want a cup of coffee?" she asked with a smile.

"We sure could use one of those," Doc Swindall replied. "I hope it tastes as good as it smells."

"Coffee never tastes as good as it smells somehow," Carrie said, "but you are welcome to it. Breakfast will be on the board soon. Caleb is out doing the milking and feeding the animals. He'll be back soon."

"Hits dark as pitch out there," said John Branham. "Don't hardly see how he can get his chores done."

"Oh, he carries a lantern and has a couple more hanging in the barn that he lights," Carrie smiled. "He's used to fumbling around in the dark."

Caleb McHenry came through the door with a bucket of milk in his hand. He had a scarf tied around his head and his hat was pulled down as low as it would go. "It's mighty cold out there this morning," he said. "Kinda felt good to snuggle up against the old cow while I was milking. She generates some warmth."

The Virginia boys got a chuckle out of that, but they did not like hearing that it was cold outside. They knew they were going to be leaving the warmth of the house soon.

"You all sit down now," said Carrie. "The ham and eggs are ready and I'll be getting the johnny cakes up soon."

Once Caleb had blessed the food, Cap Hall, Doc Swindall, and John Branham enjoyed the best breakfast they had consumed in quite a while. Everything was just perfect. None of them were used to such cooking, even at home. It was a feast that they would remember.

"We're gonna have to take off soon as we can," said Cap Hall. "I am hoping we can make it to this place called Summersville today."

"Oh, I think you can," said Caleb. "It's a good hike but if you stay with it, you should be there by nightfall, maybe before."

As they were getting ready to go out the door Carrie gave Cap Hall a linen bag. "This might taste good around noon," she said. "It's some biscuits and ham. If you keep it inside your coat, maybe it wouldn't get so cold. Walking in this kind of weather will soon burn up your energy."

"Well, we're certainly much obliged for that and for all of your hospitality," Cap replied. "You two are the nicest folks we've met on this journey."

The posse members all had on long underwear, heavy clothing, and a hat that came down over their ears. But as they had already learned, if the wind picked up a little, it cut right through all of the layers. They had also learned that if they walked at a fast pace, it helped to keep them warm. They were on the road just a little after dawn. It was cold but after they had topped the first mountain they began to warm up.

"Them sure was some nice folks, them McHenrys," said John Branham. "Till we got with them I was beginning to think there weren't no nice folks up here."

"They's fine folks all right," Cap Hall replied, "but he was a Bible spout'n son-of-a-bitch weren't he? I think he was about half preacher. He kinda made me unsettled with all of his preaching and praying. But that woman set a good table, damned if she didn't."

Doc Swindall finally chimed in with his opinion. "I don't care how much Bible he spouted. I think I could have stayed there a week or more if'n they would have kept me. Besides, Cap, a little pray'n ain't gonna hurt you none. Might do you some good! If'n there really is a hell, I'd say you are on a fast train headed in that direction."

Cap Hall looked at Doc Swindall with a half grin. "It's a wonder they kept you as long as they did. You ate like a 1600-pound workhorse and you ain't got no table manners a-tall. If'n I'm on the way to hell I'd say you'll be close behind me."

Some time around ten o'clock that morning the posse came to the Weston-Gauley Bridge Turnpike and headed northeast toward Summersville. The Turnpike was not a very good road, but it was the best road they had been on since they left Bluefield. It wasn't long until they realized that it was also more heavily traveled than the roads they had walked previously. Even though it was a cold January morning, they met a few people on saddle horses right away. They all nodded and spoke but they had their collars on their coats turned up with their chin buried in as far as it would go. It was no morning for casual conversation with strangers.

The posse had covered perhaps four or five miles on the Turnpike when they came upon a man traveling toward them trying to get a team of horses and a wagon through a long hole of water. The hole had been frozen over but the horses had broken through the ice and the wagon had become bogged down. The driver was whipping them with a leather strap. The horses would lunge into their harnesses with every lick from the strap, but the wagon was not moving.

Cap Hall approached the driver and spoke to him.

"Aire you stuck?" asked Cap.

"Fraid so," the driver replied. "I think it's mostly the right front wheel that is holding us."

"Do you have airy a saw with you?" John Branham asked.

"Yes, I do," said the driver. "I always carry a crosscut saw because there is sometimes a tree or limb in the road somewhere."

"Get it out of there. I'll saw us a pry bar out of the woods here and maybe we can lift a little over that wheel and git you going."

John Branham and Doc Swindall took the saw into the woods

and came back with a white oak pole about ten feet long and six inches through. They positioned the pole under the wagon right behind the wheel that was stuck.

"Now when we lift her up a little, whoop them horses and we'll see if she breaks out." said John Branham.

All three of the Virginia men took hold of the pole and lifted with all their might. The driver yelled and struck one of the horses with the strap and the wagon broke free. He kept whipping and yelling until the horses had the wagon free of the entire water hole.

He got down from his wagon and walked back to the posse and shook each of their hands. "Don't know what I would have done if you boys hadn't come along," he said. "I sure appreciate it."

"Weren't much trouble," said Cap Hall. "We were glad to oblige. We're headed to Summersville. You think we can make it afore dark?"

"Oh, I'd say you could, but you won't be able to loaf around any. You'll have to keep on get'n it. You sure I don't I owe you boys anything?"

"No, hell no," said Cap Hall. "We were just glad to help you out."

# INCIDENT AT KESLERS CROSS LANES

The posse set a pretty good pace for the next leg of their journey. They tried to make the best of the short days and did not tarry too long at any one place. The sun had already dropped over the ridges by a little after 4:00 p.m. and it was getting colder by the minute.

Cap Hall took a look at the clearing sky. "We might ought to start looking for a place to roost again," he said. "It feels like it's a-gonna get bitter cold tonight and I ain't a-want'n to have to hump up along the road somewheres."

"I'd say you are right about that," John Branham replied. "It sure would be nice to find a warm place to sleep."

Doc Swindall was always willing to go along with finding a place to sleep, and even more interested in finding a place to eat.

They came to a small village called Cross Lanes just south of Summersville and Cap Hall spotted a house that looked promising. They approached the house and knocked on the door.

A man with a warm smile answered the knock. He was an older man, perhaps in his seventies. But he looked hale and hearty. He could see that his visitors were shivering cold so he invited them in. The posse stepped to the woodstove before they uttered a word.

"It's mighty cold a-walking," Doc Swindall said as he nodded to their host.

"Where you boys from?" the host inquired.

"We come from down in Virginia," Cap Hall replied. "We're lawmen, on the track of some killers that we have reason to believe are up in this area."

Cap got his letter of authorization out of his jacket before the host managed a reply, and handed it to him. "We're representing the sheriff of Wise County."

"That's a pretty fur piece ain't it?" the old man asked.

"Hit's a hike, that's fur sure," Cap Hall replied. "We been a'walk'n for about five days, but I think we are a'git'n close. We've walked all the way from Bluefield. You ever heard of a place called Boggs?"

"I know just where it is," the old man replied.

"That's where we are a-head'n," said Cap. "We have information that these murdering scalawags are holed up there."

"Well your journey is about over," said the man. He extended his hand and shook with each of them. "My name is Conner McClung," he said.

"Don't suppose you would have a warm place where we could spend the night?" Cap Hall inquired.

"Well, as you can see, this is a small place. I live here by myself so I don't need much room. I ain't really got no place to put you, but I know some folks just up the road who would probably keep you for the night."

As they warmed themselves and talked to the old gentleman, Cap Hall asked if he might know someone nearby who might pilot them into the Boggs area.

"I don't know such a person," said Mr. McClung, "but if you tell these folks where I am sending you, I think they'll be glad to help you."

The posse sat around and talked with the kindly old gentleman for a while longer, and bad as they hated to strike out in the cold again, they moved on toward the suggested house.

But as they were making their way, John Branham spotted a good-sized log house surrounded by a fairly large apple orchard.

"That looks like a place that has some extra room in it. Let's see if we might be able to stay there." They all agreed and walked over to the nice looking cabin. A heavy-set man with a beard met them at the door.

"Come in out of that cold wind," he offered. "It's too cold a night to stand out there in the weather."

After they got inside and warmed themselves by the fire, Cap Hall introduced himself and his companions and explained their situation. As had become his custom, he showed his credentials.

"My name is Edwin Buck," the man said. "As you can see, I live here alone and I have some room. I'd be glad to put you up for the night. I wouldn't turn any man out in weather like this."

After they had talked a bit and removed their coats, the man put them all in one room. There was one bed and a lounge-like piece of furniture against the other wall. Cap Hall and Doc Swindall slept in the bed. John Branham found a place on the lounge. But the posse was not in for a restful night.

Some time in the middle of the night, five men came crashing into the cabin. All of them had guns and the guns were pointed at the Virginia posse. The intruders said there was a reward out for a man, and they believed that man in question was one of them.

Cap Hall looked at the men in disbelief. "You boys are badly mistaken," he said.

"None of us are the man you are looking for. We are all from down in Virginia." He again showed the letter authorizing them as deputies from Wise County.

Once the mistaken identity was agreed upon the men became very interested in the mission of the Virginia posse. One of them, John Halstead, said he knew the Birch River country and knew where Boggs was located. Although he did not tell the posse immediately, he also thought he knew where the Fleming brothers were staying. He had learned during a visit up that way that two men from Virginia were staying with their brother-in-law near Boggs.

The members of the Virginia posse did not have much money, but they offered the man a ladies watch that John Branham was carrying with him if he would guide them to Boggs. Halstead looked the watch over carefully and agreed to go. But one of the members of the group who had crashed into the cabin wanted to know why three of them were needed to arrest just two men. "I could do it myself," he boasted. With that comment, Cap Hall provided a little background on the Fleming brothers.

"I doubt that any one person could arrest these two boys," he said. "The Fleming boys are no one to fool with. They'll kill you in a minute. They have already killed several men down in our area, including the outright massacre of five people. There was one group of five men who tracked them down in the mountains and four out of five of them got killed. The Fleming boys did not get hurt much at all. Calvin is especially fast with a gun. I would say that any man who gets into a confrontation with those Fleming boys is not going to come out of it without getting hit. Their daddy, Jefferson Fleming was meaner than his sons. They say he killed a man and took his wife when he was young. Henan and Calvin have fought, killed or evaded, some twenty-two men who have tried to bring them in."

Cap Hall's description of the Fleming brothers brought looks of consternation from the men. No one else boasted that they could go take them alone. Cap made believers out of them.

The next morning the Virginia posse set out with John Halstead to locate the Fleming brothers. It was another bitter cold day and they had a long walk ahead of them. But the Virginia posse felt much more confident about their mission at this point because they at least knew where they were going and didn't feel like they were wandering aimlessly around the West Virginia mountains.

The area around Summersville featured some open country but once they passed through it and started the long climb up Powells Mountain they were passing through some of roughest looking country they had seen.

# THE CULTURE OF BIRCH RIVER

Henan and Calvin were not living like hermits at Boggs. They had been in the Boggs/Tioga area for a little more than three months and had gotten to know several people. No one there, other than their immediate relatives, had the slightest inkling of their background or previous criminal behavior. The boys were behaving like model citizens.

During the months of November and December they had worked three or four, sometimes five days a week for the sawmill owner, William Roberts, up at Tioga. But the January weather turned very cold and they were not working as much. They had gone up a few times and helped Mr. Roberts with farm chores but he was not sawing any timber. They had been hanging around the Boggs area, just trying to stay warm. The Birch River had mostly frozen over in early January except the sections that flowed swiftly. They always went down to the Boggs Post Office on Saturday to check the mail.

The Boggs Post Office and store was the gathering place for the area residents, especially on Saturday afternoons. That's when most folks had time to come to the store to pick up a few supplies and to do some visiting. Sometimes there would be music provided by a local fiddler by the name of Carpenter. A banjo player named Fred Cool usually joined him. They played tunes that the Fleming boys had never heard of, probably because Mr. Carpenter and his family made most of them up. The tunes had strange sounding names such as *Yew Piney Mountain*, *Shelv'n Rock*, *Old Christmas Morning*, and Henan's favorite, *Camp Chase*. According to Mr. Carpenter, one of his relatives won his freedom at the old Yankee prison camp in Ohio because he made up *Camp Chase* and played it in a fiddle contest. Prison officials had promised that the person who played the best fiddle tune could go home. Calvin and Henan both liked the old mountain fiddle tunes so they would sit around and listen as long as the musicians played. Once in a while someone in the store would get up and do a little flatfoot step to one of the tunes.

One of the men in the store told Calvin that Mr. Carpenter rode his horse several miles on Saturday morning just so he could get to play music with Fred Cool. He would wrap his fiddle in some linen, put it in an old burlap sack, and tie it to his saddle. Fred Cool's old banjo was crude and did not have keys around the edge so it could be tightened. So, when he came into the store he would hold his banjo up to the fire to tighten the head before he tuned it. It was a better-looking banjo than the one Caleb Johnson had, but it did not appear to be factory built. The cold weather was hard on the instruments but once the two men and their instruments got acclimated, they soon spread some warmth into the old store building.

There was also usually a checker game or two going on. The storekeeper provided the checkerboards. Calvin was a good checker player and sometimes got into the games but Henan just watched.

More than anything else the store building that housed the post office was just a warm place to gather during the bitter cold of January. The January of 1894 had been especially cold but there had not been a lot of snow. The frozen ground made for easy winter traveling but the temperature had been below zero just about every night. Daytime temperatures rarely made it into the thirties.

Most Saturday afternoons would find fifteen or twenty people in the rather small store building that measured about fourteen by eighteen feet. There was a counter on one side and the post office was located in the corner near the door. There were some nail kegs and a couple of crude chairs positioned around the woodstove.

Those who loafed away the day at the store were all men. But there was always several women going in and out all day. Henan liked to look them over and every now and then engaged one of them in conversation. A rather attractive lady by the name of Nellie Bennett flirted with him a little one Saturday early in January and tried to get him to come to the church. She stopped in front of the nail keg that he was sitting on and looked Henan straight in the eye.

"Mr. Johnson, why don't you and your brother come down to the church in the morning. We'd all like to see you there."

Henan was a little surprised and for a moment or two, nearly speechless. Finally, he came up with a response.

"My brother and I ain't never been very religious," he said. "I don't know if'n I've ever been inside a church. I think Frank's been in church some, back when he was court'n the girls. But I don't think either one of us would know how to act if we come down there."

"You don't have to act any certain way," Nellie replied. "Folks just sing and pray a little. The preacher does most of the talking."

"I wouldn't know the words to any of the songs," said Henan. "I ain't much of a singer no way."

"We have song books," Nellie replied. "You can read, can't you?"

"Yeah, I read pretty good, finished the sixth grade, but I ain't no singer."

"Well, you don't have to be a great singer. Do you believe in God?" Nellie asked.

"Oh, I guess I do. Somebody had to put us on this earth, I reckon. I just never think about it much."

"Maybe you ought to think about it some," said Nellie. "If you don't, the devil will get you shore."

"Well, I'll talk to Frank about it," Henan lied. "Maybe we'll come down one Sunday."

She started to walk away, then hesitated and gave Henan another look. "Has anyone ever told you boys that you talk kinda funny," she asked?

"How's that we talk funny?" Henan returned the question.

"Well, up here when we talk about the stuff that grows on people's heads, we call it *hair*. You boys say *hyar*, or something like that. Same thing with *there*. You all say *thar*. And I don't even know how to spell what you boys call a *house*. It sounds like *hoase*."

"Now, that's kinda interesting," Henan replied with his wry smile. "My brother and I were just talking the other day about how folks up this way say their words funny. Could be that you folks have it wrong?"

"I don't think so," Nellie replied. "I ain't never heard nobody talk like you two."

"Well, maybe if we hang around long enough we'll learn to talk like you."

Nellie did not respond to that. She just turned and walked away.

Henan watched Nellie Bennett walk out of the store and decided that she was pleasing to look at. He didn't think she was worth going to church for. But it occurred to him that when the weather warmed up, she might be worth a look. Calvin, who was playing checkers, had overheard the conversation. He looked at Henan, smiled, and shook his head.

One Saturday the storekeeper surprised Calvin a little with a question about the two guns that he carried. Calvin always carried a .44 in a shoulder holster and .32 caliber Colt stuck in his belt. Henan also carried his .44 in a shoulder holster. For good measure he carried a .38 inside the top of his right boot.

"How come you boys carry so many guns?" he asked. "Are you expecting trouble?"

"No, not that I know of," Calvin replied. "I guess we are just used to carrying them. There's some mean people down where we come from, especially them damned moonshiners, so you never know what to expect from them. Me and my brother learnt a long time ago that if you carry a pistol where everybody can see it, you won't have no trouble."

"But why the second gun?" the storekeeper continued.

"Well, I reckon they ain't no reason in particular. It's just a comfort fer me to hav'em both."

"I don't think anyone around Boggs is going to give you any

trouble," said the storekeeper. "Folks around here are pretty peaceable."

"Yeah, I've noticed that," said Calvin. "Maybe when I get more used to being around decent folks, I'll stop tote'n these things around. But I love my .44."

"Guess there ain't no harm in carrying them anyway," said the storekeeper. "I was just curious."

## THE POSSE CLOSES IN

The Virginia posse was nearing the end of its relentless pursuit of the Fleming brothers. The long trek up Powells Mountain was made in bitter cold weather with a fairly strong wind. John Halstead, their newly acquired partner, assured them that he could make arrangements for them to stay at a home near Boggs so they could get organized before they actually went after the Wise County killers.

None of the posse members carried a rifle. They were all packing .44 handguns. Cap Hall, no stranger to armed pursuits, was aware of the fact that the arrest and possible gun battle would be at close quarters. When they arrived at the community of Birch River they talked to the same man that Calvin and Henan had talked with when they came through back in August. The posse was a rough looking crew. None of them had taken a bath for seven or eight days, nor had they shaved. The bitter cold weather had kept the body odor down, but they were a mangy lot to be sure.

The posse had gone into the store mostly to get warm. They held out their hands and warmed them by the woodstove. Cap Hall again reminded the members of the posse that they were going to be walking into a very dangerous situation.

"I guess, we are within a few miles of Boggs," he said. "I just want to remind everyone that this is not going to be easy. We'll try to arrest the boys and take'em back to Wise County. But as you all know, they have so far put up a strong fight every time someone has tried to bring'em in. So I want everyone to be ready to start shoot'n…and shoot'n to kill if'n they decide to put up a fight. I don't think I have to tell either of you boys that Calvin and Henan are both good with a gun."

"We both know that all too damned well," said John Branham. "We need to plan what we are going to do pretty careful. I'd hate to think I walked all the way up here, froze my ass off, and half starved to death, just to get shot."

Doc Swindall pulled off his hat and rubbed the back of his neck. "I think we just ought to go in shoot'n. You know damned well they ain't going to give up."

"We can't do that," said Cap Hall. "They'll probably be witnesses and we would just look like plain murderers. We've got to make this attempted arrest look legal and proper. I don't think it says 'dead or alive' anywhere on the Wise County posters. But I ain't got a thing agin shoot'n the hell out of both of them. They got it com'n."

Their newly acquired member, John Halstead, listened and decided that he did not want any part of the arrest attempt. But he came up with a suggestion. "I'd say that your best bet is to walk on up to the house where we are going to stay. I'll go ahead into Boggs and make sure that the Fleming boys are still around the area. You boys can just lay low until I get back with a report. Then we can come up with a plan."

The posse all agreed with Halstead's plan and they set out on another cold walk, this time up Birch River. When they arrived at the house where Halstead had arranged for them to stay, Halstead walked on to Boggs and paid a visit to the post office.

"Do you happen to know of two gentlemen who recently came into this area from down in Virginia who go by the name of Fleming? They are brothers and both are in their twenties."

"I know of two boys who are staying with their brother-in-law just down the road here, but they don't go by the name of Fleming. They call themselves Walter and Frank Johnson. That's how they get their mail. Their letters come from Wise, Virginia. They've been working at a sawmill up at Tioga."

"That would be the men I'm trying to locate," Halstead replied.

"Do they ever come down here to the store?"

"Oh yes, they come down just about every Saturday and pick up their mail."

"Thank you, that's what I needed to know," said Mr. Halstead.

"They're still here," John Halstead reported when he got back to the house where the posse was staying. "The postmaster, Billy Boggs, told me that they have been working some at a sawmill up at Tioga and that they came to the post office just about every Saturday to pick up their mail and to loaf with the locals. He said that they were staying with their brother-in-law, a Mr. Thomas, who lived less than a mile or so from the post office."

"Maybe we just ought to go up to the house where they are staying and arrest them on the spot," Doc Swindall suggested.

"I don't know about that," Cap Hall replied. "Hit's hard to tell what we'd git into thar. That brother-in-law would probably help'em for shore and we'd have three guns to deal with instead of two. Maybe we could catch'em on the way in to the post office and arrest them in the road."

"I'd say that's pretty damned risky," said John Branham. "We know what happened down in Wise County when a posse tried to arrest them out in the mountains. They killed four of 'em. I'd say they'd start shooting and jump into the woods or over the riverbank. Thar's too many things to git behind out in the woods."

"Yeah, I guess you're probly right about that," Cap Hall replied. "Anyway, I figure that we would be way ahead to arrest them whar there are some witnesses. They'd be less likely to resist and start shoot'n if'n thar's a crowd around."

John Halstead said that he thought the post office would be a good place to arrest the boys. The postmaster had told him that Saturday afternoon usually attracted a good crowd of loafers so there should be lots of people around. "If you could walk in and catch them off guard, you could probably arrest them before they had a chance to offer any resistance."

"I think that's the best idy," said Cap Hall. "Maybe we could walk in early in the morning and kinda check the situation out, maybe find a place where we could watch them come in, and then go into the post office and confront'm."

That evening the posse spent an hour or so checking out their guns, making sure that they were working properly. Cap Hall was probably the best gunman in the group but the other two were also quite competent. But Cap had another advantage. He had the most nerve. He had been shot at before. He had killed men before. He was a mean, tough guy.

All of the members of the posse spent a sleepless night. Even though they felt pretty confident that they could pull off the arrest of the Fleming boys, there was always that chance that something could go wrong.

# THE SHOOTOUT

Early Saturday morning, January 24, 1894, Ed (Cap) Hall, John (Gooseneck) Branham, and E.J. (Doc) Swindall walked into Boggs and checked out the post office. They immediately decided that they needed to let the Fleming boys get inside the store before they made a move. They did not tell the postmaster what they were doing. They stepped outside to discuss what they were going to do.

"I don't think we need to be inside the building when they come in. They will recognize us as soon as they come through the door. So we'd better find us a place to hide outside the building," Cap Hall suggested.

"For Christ's sake, Cap," said Doc Swindall. "It's blue-assed cold out there this morning and we might have to wait hours before they come in. We'd be too damned cold to shoot if'n we had to."

"That's a good point," John Branham chimed in. "Ain't there someplace inside we can stay till they arrive?"

After making some inquiries, Cap Hall talked to the people in a house across the street from the post office. He got permission to stay inside their house so they could watch out the window for the arrival of the brothers. As it turned out they had a few hours to wait. The longer they waited the more nervous they became.

"Hell, they may not come in at all," said Doc Swindall. "Then what the hell we gonna do?"

"We'll just have to come up with another plan," Cap Hall answered.

"Yeah, but that postmaster knows we are here, knows we are looking for them, and he's liable to talk."

"I don't think so," said Cap. "He seems like a sincere and reliable man."

The three men stood by the window all morning, keeping a close eye on the road. Doc Swindall was the first to see the Fleming boys as they rode their horses down the road toward the post office. "I see them coming," he said with a quiver in his voice.

They watched as Henan and Calvin dismounted and started to tie their horses to the hitching post at the store building. Calvin's horse acted up and kept jerking away from the hitching post. Calvin slapped the horse across it's haunches a few times with the long end of his bridle reigns and finally got him under control.

"I thought he was gonna kill that horse," Doc Swindall said nervously. Doc thought he could see a pistol bulging under Calvin's coat as he struggled with his mount. The posse watched carefully as Calvin and Henan entered the post office building. As soon as they boys closed the door behind them, the posse made its move.

The Fleming brothers went straight to the post office window and were handed a letter from the postmaster, Billy Boggs. Calvin opened the letter and was starting to read with Henan looking over his shoulder. The Virginia posse came crashing through the door, guns already cocked and ready for action. Thirteen other people were crowded into the small building. Some of them were between the Fleming boys and the posse, but moved when they saw the guns.

Cap Hall, pointing his gun at Calvin, who had the reputation of being the quickest gun in western Virginia, and shouted. "Hands up, you two are under arrest. Drop your guns and surrender."

But even though the Fleming boys were totally surprised, "Quick" Calvin got off the first shot and hit Cap Hall in the head. But Cap was not out of the action. He pulled himself up and fired three shots into Calvin. The shots were fatal and Calvin fell dead on the floor. By the time Calvin hit the floor, Henan had his gun in his hand. What erupted then was a fierce battle of .44 caliber pistols between Henan

Fleming and the three members of the posse.

One of the 15 shots fired by the posse in the exchange hit the surviving brother in the jaw, tearing out most of his teeth, then stuck in his shoulder. Even though he was hit, Henan shot four times and scored with each shot. Two of them hit John Branham and he fell to the floor, fatally wounded. The third and fourth shot hit Doc Swindall in the body. The fourth shot passed through Doc's windpipe and struck Cap Hall in the temple. But the velocity of that shot had slowed as it passed through Doc Swindall and just barely penetrated the surface of Cap's head. Even though blood was spurting from him in two or three places, Henan was trying to get off a fifth shot when another slug struck him. No one knows for sure which one fired the shot that hit him. That bullet hit Henan's pistol and then split. Part of it went into the cylinder, making the gun useless. The other part of the slug ran up Henan's arm, just under the skin, and went out at his elbow.

But Henan was not quite finished. He grabbed for the other gun that he was carrying. This day he was carrying the .32 Colt that belonged to Calvin. He had stuck in his belt that morning. But before he could get a shot off, he passed out from the loss of blood and slid down with his back against the counter. Cap Hall glanced at his two partners, now down on the floor.

"You've killed my men, you son-of-bitch, and now I'm going to kill you like I killed Calvin."

But one of the men in the store restrained Cap from getting off the shot and assured him that they would tie Henan up.

It was later learned that when the posse came crashing into the Boggs Post Office, Calvin and Henan were reading a letter from someone down in Wise County which said, "Watch out, Cap Hall, John Branham and Doc Swindall are coming after you."

Miraculously, not one of the thirteen bystanders got hit by the barrage of gunfire. Some of them managed to get out the front door before the shooting started; some of them dived to the floor or sought refuge behind barrels.

Doc Swindall was hit at least twice and was losing a lot of blood when the battle ended. There was also blood coming from his mouth. He said that he thought for sure that he was dying, but he survived. John Branham was very badly wounded and could not be moved.

After Cap Hall explained the circumstances and showed the onlookers the letter of authorization, the locals handcuffed Henan. It was decided that he should be transported by wagon to the Nicholas County jail. The road from Boggs back to Birch Village was hardly passable by wagon, so Henan was taken to Summersville by way of Cowen in Webster County. From Cowen, his transporters followed what was known as the Summersville and Slaven Cabin Road to the Nicholas County jail. At a time when there were no good roads in West Virginia, this particular road was what was known as an "improved dirt road."

During the transport to Cowen, Henan was still suffering. No one had taken the time to clean the wounds or to put any kind of bandage on them. It is certain that Henan had a miserable ride during the first leg of the journey to Summersville. Those who were transporting him stopped at a store in Cowen that was owned by George Herold. George's wife, Viola, took pity on Henan. She cleaned and dressed his wounds so that he would be more comfortable. "Folks should tend to the wounds of a wounded man," she said. "No matter what kind of a man he is. You can't just let him suffer."

Henan was transported on to the Nicholas County jail and was housed there while he recovered from his wounds. He got some medical attention from a doctor in Summersville and eventually had a full recovery.

During his interment at the Nicholas County jail, word came into the area that members of Henan's family down in Virginia were on their way to break him out. The reputation of the Fleming family that had filtered into the area caused great fear among Nicholas County officials. They decided that Henan should be moved to Charleston in order to prevent any violence.

So Henan was moved, again by wagon. He was taken to

Charleston under the cover of darkness and was housed in the Kanawha County jail. He was considered a very dangerous desperado and every precaution was taken.

Cap Hall and Doc Swindall stayed at Boggs until John Branham died, nine days after the shootout. Even though they tried to make arrangements to take Henan back to Wise County for trial, and to transport Branham's body back to be buried, neither of those things happened. Henan was indicted for murder by the circuit court in Webster County and John Branham was buried at Boggs in the same cemetery where Calvin was interred. Doc Swindall and Cap Hall made their way back to Wise County soon afterwards.

The final result of the big shootout at Boggs was that all of the participants were hit. Calvin was killed instantly. John Brannon died a few days later. Cap Hall and Doc Swindall were both wounded and returned to Wise County empty handed. Henan received some rather serious wounds but recovered. Ironically, Cap Hall was shot in the back and killed in Pound about one year later and the shooter was never identified. The only two members of the shootout who lived a long life to tell the tale were A.J. Doc Swindall and Henan Fleming.

## THE TRIAL OF HENAN FLEMING

Henan remained in the Kanawha County jail until November 7, 1894. He was again secretly transported back to Webster County, this time for the trial. He was moved from Charleston to Pickens in Randolph County by rail. From Pickens he was brought "through the woods" to Webster Springs for the trial which was to begin on November 9. A group of heavily armed men were placed around the vicinity of the jail to make sure there was no escape. Before the trial, Henan was brought before the judge and questioned.

"Do you have counsel for your defense?" Judge W.G. Bennett asked.

"No sir, I do not." Henan replied. "But I respectfully request that the judge appoint A.J. Horan and W.E.R Bryne to speak for me."

The judge so ordered that the two gentlemen that he requested would defend him. E.J. Morton was the prosecuting attorney for the trial.

W.E.R. Bryne, known to his friends as Bill was a widely known attorney in West Virginia. He was better known for his fishing exploits than his performance in the courtroom. He fished the Elk River from its headwaters where Big Springs Run and Old Fields Creek come together at Slaty Fork to form the Elk River to where the Elk ran into the Great Kanawha at Charleston. He wrote about his fishing exploits in the then widely read *West Virginia Wildlife Magazine*. For some reason or another, he immediately liked Henan. The two men formed a bond of sorts.

The trial was conducted in the upper floor of a store building and opened in the traditional fashion. The Circuit Court Judge, W.G Bennett, presided.

"How does the defendant plead?" the judge asked the defending attorneys.

"Not guilty." Attorney Bill Byrne replied.

Prosecutor Morton began by addressing the court about the nature of the crime and then informed the jury that, "after hearing the witnesses and the evidence, I am sure that you will deliver a verdict of guilty for Mr. Fleming." He then proceeded to call several witnesses to the stand who said they witnessed the shootout.

The first witness testified that when the posse burst into the Boggs Post Office and asked the Fleming brothers to raise their hands, Calvin immediately reached for his gun. He said he wasn't sure but he was pretty sure Calvin fired the first shot before he was killed by Cap Hall.

"Did you actually see all of the action?" the prosecutor asked.

"I saw the first few shots, then I dived for cover," the witness said. "I missed a few seconds, but I clearly saw Henan Fleming shoot John Branham." On cross-examination, Bill Byrne asked the witness if he was absolutely certain that Calvin Fleming fired the first shot.

"He might not have fired the first shot but he definitely went for his gun. I think Mr. Cap Hall had to fire to protect himself."

"Don't you suppose that Henan figured he was next and only shot to protect himself?" Attorney Byrne asked.

"I wouldn't know about that," the witness replied. "All I know is that Henan Fleming shot and killed John Branham and hit the other two members of the posse."

"No further questions," Bill Byrne replied.

During a recess in the proceedings, the prosecutor came to Bill Byrne and said that he had pretty reliable information telling him that heavily armed members of the Fleming Clan were on their way to rescue Henan and take him back home. He was afraid that they might crash into the courtroom and that several people would be at risk of getting killed.

"Furthermore," the honorable prosecutor said, "I suspect that if they could get into the courtroom, I would be the first target and would surely get killed. I want you to ask your client if there is anything to the information that has been passed to me."

"I'll be glad to ask him," attorney Byrne replied. "But I doubt that there is anything to that."

Byrne asked Henan if members of his family might be on their way to rescue him.

"No, not that I have heard about. I think the only family member present at this trial is my brother-in-law, Mr. Thomas, who is already in the courtroom. I don't think he's gonna hurt anybody."

When Byrne reported to the prosecutor what Henan had told him, Mr. Morton was skeptical.

"My informant tells me that he is pretty sure that Henan's people are on the way, or perhaps are already in the area."

Byrne pointed out Mr. Thomas and told the prosecutor that he was the only family member present. But it was obvious to Byrne that Mr. Morton was very nervous about the situation.

"That all adds up," said the prosecutor. "I'll just bet that he is here to get a reading on the situation and that he will bring the whole gang back tomorrow."

The next morning when the court convened, Mr. Thomas showed up alone and took his place in the audience. Bill Byrne noticed that the prosecutor was treading lightly as he examined and cross-examined witnesses. He was especially careful when he cross-examined Henan. He never really went for the jugular. He never used typical prosecutor language such as calling Henan a cold-blooded killer. He said unkind and disparaging things about the defense attorneys, but he treated Henan gingerly.

Bill Byrne took all of this in and decided to invoke a little more fear into the prosecutor. During the next recess, he told Henan to tell Mr. Thomas to get up and leave the courtroom when the prosecutor started his closing argument. Henan nodded for his brother-in-law to come over and did as Byrne suggested.

As soon as the prosecutor uttered his first sentence in his summary, Mr. Thomas got up and walked across the front of the room and out the door. The prosecutor followed his every step. He then toned down his closing argument to basically say that he was doing his duty as prescribed by law to prosecute and bring to justice an indicted killer. But he did not rant and rave. He never made the statement that Henan was a dangerous person and needed to be hanged.

When Byrne and A.J. Horan made their closing argument they lambasted the prosecution for trying to make a murder case out of what was obviously an act of self-defense. "Henan had just witnessed his brother being shot before his eyes. What was he supposed to do, stand there and be killed? Henan is really the heroic defender of his brother's life and is certainly no murderer." Bill Byrne concluded.

Mr. Thomas did not reappear in the courtroom and the prosecutor was still keeping a wary eye on the door. He was expecting the Fleming Clan to coming rushing through the door any moment, pistols firing away.

The jury was out for less than an hour before they returned to the courtroom with a verdict. After the jury was seated and the audience had settled down, Judge Bennett looked to the jury.

"Has the jury reached a verdict?" he asked.

"We have, your honor," the foreman of the jury replied.

"And what is that verdict?" asked the judge.

The jury foreman looked straight at Henan and said firmly, "Not Guilty!"

So Henan was acquitted. But he was not out of the woods. He still faced trial in Wise County for his part in the Pound Gap Massacre.

# FACING JUSTICE IN VIRGINIA

It had been three years since the Mullins Clan had been ambushed at Pound Gap. As is generally the case, much of the emotion surrounding the event had subsided. But in the eyes of the law, justice had still not yet been served. Henan Fleming, Calvin Fleming, Henry Adams, and Marshall Doc Taylor had all been indicted for murder in connection with the massacre, which had occurred on May 14, 1892. Only two of those indicted had experienced closure.

Marshall Taylor and been tried and hanged on October 27, 1893. Calvin had been killed in the Webster County shootout. It was now time for Henan to face the charges in Wise County. The trial began on July 24, 1895 at the Wise County Courthouse.

The prosecution was at a slight disadvantage because the indictments had been based mostly on the testimony of the one adult survivor of the massacre, Jane Mullins. She was the widow of one of the victims of the massacre, Wilson Mullins. Wilson was riding on the wagon and Jane was walking out ahead of the wagon when the firing started. Wilson was killed instantly but Jane Mullins managed to escape. She had stated at the Grand Jury that indicted the four men that she had seen the shooters very plainly. "Even though their faces were covered," she reported, "there was little doubt in her mind that the three shooters were Doc Taylor and the Fleming brothers." She said she could tell by their stance because she knew all three of them well. The shooters were less than twenty feet away so she had gotten a good look at them, according to her report. Ira's 15-year-old son was behind the wagon and ran back down the hill when the firing started. He said that he did not see the shooters.

The problem at the 1895 trial was the Jane Mullins was no longer alive to testify. She did not die of natural causes. A newspaper account of her death from nearby Dickens County printed the following:

> *Your correspondent has just learned that "Orb" Fleming, a brother to the outlaws, Cal and Henan (Fleming), shot and killed a woman in the vicinity of Pound Gap, where the Mullins family was murdered in the spring of 1892. This woman was the widow of Wilson Mullins, one of the murdered persons of that family. The report says that she was walking about the premises of her home, and was shot by someone secreted in the brush some distance from the house, and circumstances point to Fleming as the perpetrator of the foul crime. The supposed motive is that as Mrs. Mullins was the material witness in the case against Henan Fleming, she was killed to destroy this evidence against him.*

No charges were ever brought against "Orb" Fleming because there was no evidence against him. It was just all speculation. But, be that as it may, she would have been the star witness at Henan's trial had she been living.

The trial raged on for six days as the prosecution tried to build its case. But all of the evidence was circumstantial. However the prosecutor did have what he thought was an ace in the hole.

Just when things were looking good for Henan the prosecuting attorney addressed the judge. "Your Honor, I think I have the responsibility to inform the court that Henan Fleming admitted to me that he was one of the shooters at Pound Gap during one of our conversations."

"Do you have this confession in writing, signed by the accused?" the Judge asked.

"No, your honor, I do not," the prosecutor replied, "but he did make that oral statement to me."

"Is Mr. Fleming willing to take the stand and admit to murder at this point in the proceedings?" asked the Judge.

The prosecutor conferred with Henan's attorney to see if Henan was willing to make such a statement. He came back to the bench and told the judge that Mr. Fleming was not willing to do so. The judge said that he could not accept the confession unless it was made in court, or was signed by the accused. The attorney for the commonwealth then announced that without the confession he would be unable to ask for a conviction.

The jury left the room and was gone but a short while before they returned to the courtroom and announced a verdict of "Not Guilty." Henan again escaped the long arm of the law and went free.

Yet there is an unknown factor surrounding the circumstances that allowed Henan to go free at both locations. There has always been a question in the minds of those who have looked at the history of the trials. Was there a fear factor involved? There is little question that the Fleming family was quite capable of killing people, going all the way back to the father of the Fleming boys, Robert Jefferson Fleming.

An account of Robert Jefferson Fleming's death in the Clintwood, Virginia newspaper on August 21, 1893, read as follows:

*Jefferson Fleming, the father of the outlaws Cal and Henan Fleming, died at his home at the upper end of this county on Friday last, after an illness of several weeks duration. Jefferson Fleming was born in Kentucky and was 73 years old. He always led a reckless, inconsistent life and was dreaded by his neighbors as an ill-natured and disagreeable man. He has been married twice. His first wife was married when he got acquainted with her, and after a brief acquaintance, her husband was missing and to this day the fate of the poor man has not been revealed. But Fleming and this woman were married in a short time after this occurrence... He is said to have been the father of thirty-one children, several of them illegitimate...(Jefferson) was charged to have been connected with the Pound Gap murders, for which his sons were indicted. He was indicted as an accomplice...but the case was dismissed.*

So many observers have wondered that given the history of the Fleming Clan, was the fear factor influential in the Virginia judge's decision to dismiss the case against Henan? Did some member of the Fleming Clan leak word to the judge that if Henan was convicted, he might die of a sudden case of lead poisoning? No one will ever know the answer to that but it is an interesting thought to contemplate.

# THE RETURN TO WEST VIRGINIA

A few days after Henan was acquitted, he and his wife Catherine were settled back in their house. But Henan was not happy. He was restless. The broad river bottoms and the roaring Birch River beckoned to him. He missed the people he had gotten to know during his sojourn in Webster County. While he was grateful that he had been acquitted, he still had the feeling that he was no longer welcome in Wise County. One evening at the supper table he broached the subject with Catherine.

"You know, Catherine," Henan said solemnly, "I really liked it up in Webster County. The people there are as nice as they can be. Seems like everyone is friendly. Cal and I were treated kindly by just about everybody we come across. Even after the shooting, most folks were very kind to me. In fact, if'n it hadn't been for a couple of the guys in the Post Office at the time of the shooting, old Cap Hall would have finished me off. But they restrained him and told him that they would see that I was arrested. I really think I like the people up there better than I do the ones around here. I wouldn't mind a'gone back up there to live. I think folks around here have a bad opinion of me and it ain't gonna go away anytime soon."

"But what in the world would you do up there?" Catherine asked. "You have to make a living some way."

"There's plenty of work in those mountains, Catherine. I don't think I'd have a bit of trouble finding a way to make a living. That part of the country is a'start'n to take off just like it is right hyar in Wise County. There's coal mines up thar just like there is hyar. And it looks like the timber business in Webster and the other counties around it is just going to get bigger and bigger. Some man by the name of Camden has built a huge mill just a few miles from where I was a'livin up at Boggs. Hits at a place called Camden. Ain't no doubt in my mind that there will be a bunch of people moving into that country. Thar's small sawmills a'spring'n up all over the place. The brother-in-law said in one of his letters that this here huge double band saw mill that this Camden feller built is causing a big stir. He said they are going to build a big hotel in Camden and another one in a nearby town called Webster Springs. I think I could get a job in no time. I ain't helpless, you know. The only difference is I think folks in West Virginia have a different opinion of me than they do hereabouts. I think you'd feel right comfortable in Webster County. The countryside looks an awful lot like it does hyar. If'n you go up there and look about, you'll think you're home."

"I know you're not helpless, but I don't know, Henan. That's a big move I know we ain't got much, but we would have to find a way to move stuff. We ain't got no wagon. Besides, I've spent my whole life right here. I might not know how to act in West Virginia."

"We can get us a wagon some place," Henan replied. "That won't stop us. If'n we made the move when it's warm, it wouldn't be a bad trip to make. Cal and I kinda enjoyed the trip when we rode up there back in '94. Met some nice folks on the way. And, hell Catherine, a woman like you will get acquainted in no time a-tall."

"I guess it might be interesting," Catherine replied, "if I could get up the nerve to do it."

"I've been talking to my brothers," said Henan. "Al and Orbin say they might be interested in moving up there with us."

"Boy, if they would, that would make it easier for me. At least I would know somebody. It's kinda scary to think that I wouldn't know nobody but you in a strange place."

Henan and Catherine did not make the move immediately. There is no historical evidence to indicate exactly when they actually arrived in Webster County. But there is concrete evidence that they were back in West Virginia by the turn of the century. The 1900 Webster County census shows that Henan and Catherine were in Webster County as were Al and Orb Fleming. Henan listed his employment as a night watchman for one of the railroads, so he was gainfully employed. Other historical evidence indicates that all three of the brothers spent the rest of their lives in West Virginia.

Henan was correct with his prediction that Webster and the surrounding counties were on the verge of an economic boom of sorts. During the late 1890s the railroad made its way from Flatwoods to Cowen, opening up a way for the mass transportation of Webster's vast timber and coal resources. Small, independent sawmills were replaced with big corporate timber and coal operations. All kinds of spur rail lines were developed to feed into the main lines. A railroad spur even ran up Skyles Creek where Henan and Cal had worked at a sawmill during their first sojourn in West Virginia. A sizeable community developed on the very site that had once been the scene of that small-time sawmill.

As is generally the case, other economic opportunities followed in the wake of the development of the natural resources. Housing construction, blacksmith and tool shops, stables, hotels, and big general stores provided employment opportunities. The railroads also had to be built to carry the natural resources out to market. So immigrants coming into the Webster and Nicholas county areas easily found a way to make a living.

The increase in population brought growing pains. Incoming residents often had to live in tents until adequate housing was available. Many of the workers who came into the area to work in the mines and timber operations were rough men without families. Saturday nights brought plenty of heavy drinking and fights. Knife and razor fights were common.

Most of the communities that were struggling to get organized saw the need for a police force. It became very obvious that county sheriffs were spread much too thin to keep order in individual communities. As the law and order issue came to the forefront,

Henan saw an opportunity. He saw himself as being well prepared for the job. He was physically strong, tough as leather, and something of an expert with firearms. He broached the subject with Catherine one morning at breakfast.

"Catherine," he said, "I heard from some of the boys on the railroad that they are looking for policemen over in Nicholas County. They extended the railroad into a place called Cherry Tree Bottom in 1898 and that whole country over in thar is having a timber boom just like it is over hyar in Webster. A brakeman on the railroad told me that they have changed the name of Cherry Tree Bottom to Richwood and it's a'grow'n. The lumber mills are a-boom'n and people are a'mov'n in. He also tells me they are looking for rough and tumble policemen who can keep the peace. He says the pay ain't too bad. I thought I might ride over thar and take a look."

"Now what do you know about being a policeman?" Catherine asked. "You've been on the other side of the law all your life. And besides, you have a criminal record here in Webster County. Land sakes, Henan, ain't nobody gonna hire you to keep the peace."

"I ain't got no criminal record no damned place," Henan replied. "I was acquitted for every crime I've ever been tried for. Oncet a mans been acquitted, he ain't got no criminal record."

"Well, you may not have a criminal record, but you sure do have a reputation. I expect they've heard all about you over in the next county."

"It won't hurt to go over thar and talk to'em." Henan replied. "One thing I know for sure is, it takes a nervy son-of-a-bitch to be a policeman and I got plenty of that. I ain't never been afraid of nobody."

"I know you ain't afraid of nobody but I bet they won't have nothing to do with you."

The next time Henan had a couple of days off, he rode over to Richwood and inquired about getting a job as a policeman. The mayor listened intently as Henan portrayed himself as a nervy guy who had been involved in many confrontations with people.

"You are the guy who was in the big shootout over at Boggs ain't you?" the mayor inquired.

"I'm the guy," Henan replied. "Almost got myself killed. But hit was all a big mistake on the part of that posse from down in Wise County. They were after the wrong people. Cal and I were as innocent as we could be. We was just protecting ourselves. I 'spect you already know that I was acquitted."

"Yes, I know that," the mayor replied. "The truth is I do need a good strong, nervy guy to keep peace here in town. I have a couple of policemen but I guess I'd have to say they ain't doing a real good job. Sometimes they look the other way to avoid a conflict with some of the bad guys. What would you think about being the boss of the force? I could appoint you as Chief of Police and the pay would be some better."

"I'll take the job," Henan replied anxiously. "I'll start just as soon as I can get moved over from Webster County. Also, I'll have to give the railroad a little notice that I am a-leave'n."

## ON PATROL IN RICHWOOD

Henan was twenty-nine years old when the big shootout took place at Boggs. Until that time he had been something of a rake and rambling man. His name had been linked to several killings and there is adequate evidence that he was involved in the moonshine trade in western Virginia and southeastern Kentucky. But for whatever reason, Webster County had brought about a calm to his life. Even before the shootout, Henan was living a fairly straight life. But because of his wayward youth, he and Catherine got a late start in raising a family.

Once they settled in Richwood, Henan became something of a model family man, or at least it appeared so on the surface. No one really knows if he led a secret life. No one will ever know. But there is no evidence that his years as the Richwood Chief of Police were anything but exemplary.

For the most part, life was peaceful in Richwood. Yet there was a rowdy element that worked in the timber and lumber business and things sometimes got interesting on Saturday night.

Many of the men who were employed by the timber industry lived in the logging camps and came into town only rarely. But when they did, the bars enjoyed a booming business, as did the not-so-secret brothels. The logging camps were full of cocaine, a substance the loggers called "snow." When the loggers got high, fights were common and a few of those fights led to serious injuries. It did not take Henan long to realize that bringing that rowdy element under control was going to be a big part of his job.

A large portion of the loggers and mill workers were itinerants. They were just about all single and had spent most of their working lives in temporary shelters or boarding houses. They were referred to as "wood hicks." The term lumberjack that was common elsewhere in the country did not quite catch on in West Virginia. Actually, "wood hick" was a pretty accurate way to describe the itinerant loggers. "Hick" was a fairly common term used to describe a rural, uncultured, ignorant person. Since the loggers spent all of their time in the woods, the combination of the two terms was quite appropriate.

There was one "wood hick" in particular who was on a collision course with Henan. His name was Patrick McClanahan. Patrick was a big brawling Irishman who had come into the area with one of the timber companies. He stood about six foot three and weighed in the vicinity of two hundred and thirty pounds. There was no fat on his body. He was all muscle and bone. A big, broad smile was a part of his persona. There was really not much reason not to like Patrick. But when he got some liquor in him he was a different man. The slightest provocation, or oftentimes no provocation at all, would ignite his violent side. He never used anything except his hands and feet, but he had seriously injured several people who had been crazy enough to fight him.

During his first few weeks on the force Henan had not confronted McClanahan. He had always arrived too late when a fight had occurred, or a couple of times, he did not even know about it until the next day. But the moment finally came at about twilight on a Saturday night when heavy rain had caused the timber crews to shut down early. The bars were roaring by six in the evening. Word came to Henan that Patrick McClanahan had chased just about everybody out of one of the bars and busted up some of the furniture in the process. Henan strapped on his pistol, picked up his two-foot billy club, and set out alone to confront the big Irishman.

When Henan came through the door of the bar he immediately saw the broad shoulders of the Irish logger. Henan's first thought was that the McClanahan probably out weighed him forty or fifty pounds. He was alone at the bar, but there were still several patrons sitting at the tables. As Henan approached the bar McClanahan saw him in the mirrow. He turned and greeted Henan with his signature broad smile.

"I'll bet you be one Henan Fleming," the Irishman said. "I've heard about you to be sure. Of course, you know, I ain't broke no laws this evening. I'm just having a few drinks."

"And who would it be that broke up all these chairs and that table over thar?" Henan replied.

"I guess that would be me," said Patrick. "I had a slight tussle with a couple of the boys from the timber camp."

"You'll be under arrest for destruction of property," said Henan. "I hope you will walk down to the jail with me peaceably."

"I ain't going no where peaceably," Patrick responded. "I ain't done nothing wrong."

Henan spoke nary another word. He just stepped forward and whacked Patrick McClanahan across the forehead with his club, then came back the other way with a backstroke in the same spot before the Irishman knew what hit him. But Henan did not stop there. Instead of trying to retaliate, Patrick brought his hands up to try to protect his head. But Henan kept on swinging. After several strong hits to the top of his head, the big Irishman went down to his knees. He was not unconscious but he was definitely groggy. The bar tender and those sitting at the tables looked on in disbelief.

Then, for the first time since he had been hired, Henan drew his .44 caliber pistol and pointed it at McClanahan's head as he helped him to his feet.

"You walk along with me down to the jailhouse and we won't have no trouble," said Henan. "You give me the slightest reason to and I'll shoot the top of your head off."

Like a wounded duck, Patrick McClanhan struggled out of the bar ahead of Henan.

Henan housed him in the jail without incident. The next

morning, even though it was Sunday, the man who was appointed as the city judge held a short hearing for McClanahan.

"Several witnesses have said that you are guilty of breaking up furniture in the bar last evening and that you resisted arrest from an official officer of the law. You can either pay a $100 fine or spend the next five days in jail."

"I ain't got a hundred dollars," Patrick replied.

"In that case," the judge said to Henan, "escort him back to his cell."

So Patrick McClanahan spent the next five days in jail and then returned to work without incident. He had "get even" thoughts in his mind but after talking with some of the other loggers on the job, he mellowed quickly. He was told that Henan had killed several men during the course of his life and had the reputation of being an excellent shot with a pistol.

After the incident with McClanahan, Henan had little trouble keeping the peace in Richwood. All he had to do was to walk into one of the bars and a silence fell over the room. He became an effective peace officer.

When the mayor talked with Henan about the incident with McClanahan, Henan told him that he was only following the advice his father had given him when he was a young man. "He always told us," said Henan, "when you move into a new place, always look up the bully of the town and whoop the piss out of him. Then you won't have no more trouble."

# CAMDEN-ON-GAULEY

During the first decade of the twentieth century Webster County was booming. Outside industrialists with plenty of capital had come to realize that the isolated mountain areas of West Virginia held vast natural resources. As the railroads expanded in that part of the state, Webster County became one of the main targets of the big money men from a little further north. One of those developers was Johnson Newlon Camden. Camden was an affiliate of John D. Rockefeller and had made a name for himself as a high-rolling developer. He also managed to get himself elected to the United States Senate. Most historians agree that Camden's main thrust in the Senate was to pass laws that were advantageous to his business ventures. He was active in developing several big industrial projects in West Virginia.

For some reason Mr. Camden took a special interest in an area just west of Cowen and decided to build a huge mill there. One of the probable reasons that he chose that particular location was that the countryside sort of sprawled out into river bottoms along the Gauley River at that particular point. The Gauley River provided a perfect avenue for transporting timber into a mill that would be located there.

There was already a community there before the big mill was built and before the railroad had made its way that far. The community had been designated Lane's Bottom to honor some early settlers who had been killed by Indians at that location. The term Bottom was added because of the lay of the land. There was not much bottomland up river from that point but the term bottom sort of fit to be sure.

Johnson Camden also decided that the area should become a major recreation area and industrial center as well as the site of his huge lumber mill. As the town was being laid out for incorporation, Mr. Camden decided to name it after himself. But he ran into a snag. It was discovered that there was already a post office and community in Lewis County that was called Camden. The Lewis County Camden was a small rural community located near the Gilmer County line. But Johnson Camden was not to be denied. He proclaimed that the name of the town would be Camden-on-Gauley. He built a large hotel there that was to be the centerpiece of the community.

In no time at all Camden-on-Gauley became a thriving community, bringing with it all of the inevitable problems of a growing area. Henan saw opportunities developing in the new village. So he started to spend some time in Camden-on-Gauley, reconnecting with old friends and exploring possible law enforcement opportunities.

The reputation that he had built in Richwood as a tough enforcer of the law was well known in the western end of Webster County. Some time around 1915, he was designated Chief of Police of Camden-on-Gauley. In addition, memories of the big shootout at Boggs still lingered in the minds of many of the natives. And, Camden-on-Gauley had the same kind of undesirable elements that the other growing timber towns harbored during those boom years. Many of the decent folks in the town probably thought they would be safer with a man like Henan enforcing the law.

So it was in the western end of Webster County that Henan and Catherine raised their family. Henan became something of a pillar of the community and soon began investing some of his money in timber. Toward the end of his productive years he became a buyer and seller of timber and enjoyed a fairly prosperous life.

As Henan was walking his beat in Camden-on-Gauley one evening he chanced to meet Bill Byrne, the attorney who defended him at the Webster Springs trial. He had not seen him for several years, but they immediately recognize each other.

"You have to be Bill Byrne," Henan said as he extended his hand.

"And you are the notorious Henan Fleming," Byrne responded. "Haven't seen you in a while."

"It has been at least a month of Sundays," said Henan. "How have you been?"

"I've been just fine, but I think the question is, how have you been? I must say I have heard good things about you since you have been back in our fair state."

"I guess I've had some good fortune and a little luck," said Henan, "but I'd have to say that none of my recent good fortune would have been possible without your effort in Webster Springs. I want you to know that I still appreciate what you did for me."

"Well," Byrne responded, "I guess, as they say, I was just doing my job. But I had faith in you and highly suspected that things would turn out right for you."

Henan reached down and pulled a pretty little .32 caliber pistol out of his boot. "I always felt like I didn't pay you enough so I would like to give you this little pistol as a token of my appreciation. It's the one I pulled at the gunfight but never got a chance to use. I passed out before I could pull the trigger."

"Yes, I remember the story," said Bill Byrne. "Are you sure you want to give it up? It must mean something to you."

"Actually, the pistol belonged to Calvin. I was just carrying it that particular day. But I want you to have it."

Byrne took the pistol and cherished it for a few years. He later learned that Calvin's son wanted the gun so he looked him up and gave it to him.

Catherine Fleming died in 1926. Henan lived until 1943 and died at the age of 78.

Both are buried in a cemetery at Cottle in Nicholas County.

***Author's historical comparison:*** Many readers of this story may come away with the notion that Henan Fleming's transition from an outlaw and killer to an exemplary officer of the law is highly unusual and not believable. But all you need to do is to turn your attention to the old west. A high percentage of the famous U.S. Marshals and sheriffs of the old west were ex-gunfighters, outlaws, and outright killers. Wyatt Earp himself was no model citizen before or after the Gunfight at the OK Corral. Henan Fleming never got the notoriety of any of the famous western lawmen, but he was evidently just as courageous and just as effective.

# ABOUT THE AUTHOR

Mack Samples was born and raised in Corton, West Virginia, a rural community near the Kanawha/Clay County lines.

After a four-year stint in the United States Navy he entered Glenville State College and graduated with an A.B. Degree. He taught three years in West Virginia public schools, and then got a Master's Degree in History and Political Science from Ohio University. Mack worked for the University of South Carolina for five years as a professor and administrator. He then returned to Glenville State College and served as Registrar and Director of Admissions for 21 years. The final five years of his professional life was spent as a West Virginia University Extension Agent in Clay County.

Since his retirement in 1999 Mack has enjoyed some success as a writer and currently has seven books on the market, some fiction and some non-fiction.

Mack has always been involved in traditional music. His band, The Samples Brothers, has been active since 1978 and still performs on the festival circuit and other venues. He is well known as a traditional square dance caller. He and his wife, Thelma, are also ballroom dancers. They live on a 55-acre spread in Duck, WV.

During the 2003 Vandalia Festival in Charleston, West Virginia, Mack was presented with the Vandalia Award, the state's highest award for the preservation of traditional life in the Mountain State.

Mack and Thelma are the parents to two children, Tracy and Grayson, and have two grandchildren, Emma Grace and Amelia Julianne Samples.